Teaching Mathematics Through Problem-Solving

This engaging book offers an in-depth introduction to teaching mathematics through problem-solving, providing lessons and techniques that can be used in classrooms for both primary and lower secondary grades. Based on the innovative and successful Japanese approaches of Teaching Through Problem-solving (TTP) and Collaborative Lesson Research (CLR), renowned mathematics education scholar Akihiko Takahashi demonstrates how these teaching methods can be successfully adapted in schools outside of Japan.

TTP encourages students to try and solve a problem independently, rather than relying on the format of lectures and walkthroughs provided in classrooms across the world. *Teaching Mathematics Through Problem-Solving* gives educators the tools to restructure their lesson and curriculum design to make creative and adaptive problem-solving the main way students learn new procedures. Takahashi showcases TTP lessons for elementary and secondary classrooms, showing how teachers can create their own TTP lessons and units using techniques adapted from Japanese educators through CLR. Examples are discussed in relation to the Common Core State Standards, though the methods and lessons offered can be used in any country.

Teaching Mathematics Through Problem-Solving offers an innovative new approach to teaching mathematics written by a leading expert in Japanese mathematics education, suitable for pre-service and in-service primary and secondary math educators.

Akihiko Takahashi is an Associate Professor at DePaul University, where he teaches mathematics and mathematics education. He has over forty years of first-hand experience in TTP, as well as Japanese Lesson Study, and was one of the leading mathematics teachers in Japan. Since the late 1980s, he has continued to serve as both a writer and editor of Japanese mathematics textbook series, including the best-selling mathematics textbook *Atarashii Sansuu (New Mathematics for Elementary School)*, published in Japan by Tokyo Shoseki.

Studies In Mathematical Thinking and Learning
Alan H. Schoenfeld, Series Editor

Teaching Mathematics Through Problem-Solving

A Pedagogical Approach from Japan

Akihiko Takahashi

Routledge
Taylor & Francis Group

NEW YORK AND LONDON

First published 2021
by Routledge
52 Vanderbilt Avenue, New York, NY 10017

and by Routledge
2 Park Square, Milton Park, Abingdon, Oxon, OX14 4RN

Routledge is an imprint of the Taylor & Francis Group, an informa business

© 2021 Taylor & Francis

Library of Congress Cataloging-in-Publication Data
Names: Takahashi, Akihiko (Professor of Mathematics), author.
Title: Teaching mathematics through problem-solving : a pedagogical
    approach from Japan / Akihiko Takahashi.
Description: New York, NY : Routledge, 2021. | Series: Studies
    in mathematical thinking and learning series | Includes
    bibliographical references and index.
Identifiers: LCCN 2020043943 | ISBN 9780367858810 (hardback) |
    ISBN 9780367858827 (paperback) | ISBN 9781003015475 (ebook)
Subjects: LCSH: Problem solving—Study and teaching. |
    Mathematics—Study and teaching.
Classification: LCC QA63 .T34 2021 | DDC 510.71—dc23
LC record available at https://lccn.loc.gov/2020043943

ISBN: 978-0-367-85881-0 (hbk)
ISBN: 978-0-367-85882-7 (pbk)
ISBN: 978-1-003-01547-5 (ebk)

Typeset in Goudy
by Apex CoVantage, LLC

For my wife, Reiko

Contents

Figures

Acknowledgments

This book is a product of the tireless efforts of Japanese teachers and researchers working to improve mathematics teaching and learning. From the late 1970s to the 1990s, I was fortunate to be heavily involved in the Japanese education reform movement which established the specialized pedagogical approach known as *Mondai Kaketsu Gakushuu*, or "Teaching Through Problem-Solving (TTP)," as a widespread pedagogical approach. It was a long journey to incorporate problem-solving as an integral part of the mathematics curriculum, but now this approach has become a mainstream pedagogy in Japan for teaching mathematics, especially in the elementary grades. During that time, I was privileged to work with Japan's teacher leaders of mathematics, including Takeshi Matsuyama, Kozo Tsubota, Yojiro Nakano, Takashi Nakamura, and Shunji Kurosawa, to develop, exchange, and share ideas about how to use problem-solving in mathematics classrooms. The examples of TTP lessons in this book largely come from my collaborations with these teacher leaders. Mathematics education researchers, including Yoshishige Sugiyama, Toshiakira Fujii, Yoshinori Shimizu, Toshio Sawada, and Yoshihiko Hashimoto, provided guidance as I established the theoretical background of my work and supported me as I became a mathematics education researcher myself. In the U.S., I have been fortunate in having the strong support of the Chicago Lesson Study Group leadership team and their schools, and the Mills College Lesson Study Group, Catherine Lewis and Shelley Friedkin, and its partner schools in the San Francisco Unified School District and the Oakland Unified School District. Without these collaborations with Japanese and U.S. practitioners and researchers, this book would never exist. I also want to thank Toshiakira Fujii, Tad Watanabe, and Tom McDougal. They shared their wisdom on Japanese and U.S. mathematics education by reviewing my early drafts and providing critical feedback. And special thanks go to my editor Kate Beckwitt, whose contributions have been innumerable and invaluable.

Series Editor's Foreword

There's something special about mathematics teaching in Japan. Having worked with and admired my Japanese colleagues for some time, I think I can identify three main dimensions to what makes it special.

The first is really thoughtful attention to the mathematics that students are expected to learn. In very serious and careful ways, my Japanese colleagues have taken to heart the process standards in the original NCTM Standards and subsequent standards documents—problem-solving, reasoning, mathematical connections, communicating with mathematics, and using mathematical representations in the service of all of the above. That leads to a richer, deeper engagement with mathematics. Problems do not serve as exercises as they tend to in the U.S. and elsewhere, but as introductions to rich mathematical ideas. Given a problem, how can I think about the situation described? How can I make sense of it? What does it connect to? In that sense, "problem-solving" takes on the deeper meaning of learning to think mathematically.

The second is comparably deep attention to student thinking. A key issue is always how students will make sense of the mathematics and how to arrange a lesson so that students can develop meaningful understandings of the content. What are they likely to notice, how can that be built on? How can student thinking be provoked in useful ways? How can it be given "air-time" so that the whole class gets to grapple with key ideas, comparing and contrasting them, making connections, and ultimately pulling the strands of understanding together in coherent ways? Curriculum and teaching in Japan often exemplify the maxim "less is more," with fewer problems explored in much greater depth, and students learning more because they're the ones making the connections. The focus on rich mathematics and student thinking are at the heart of Teaching Through Problem-solving (TTP), the theme of this book.

Of course, teaching in this way doesn't come naturally if you've learned to teach by the "apprenticeship of observation" in the West, where problems aren't often problems as described here and teaching is more prescriptive. Planning and orchestrating mathematically rich conversations is a rare skill, and teachers don't often do collective planning and reflecting. The third dimension to Japanese teaching and learning is communal support. In Japanese schools teachers get together to work on these ideas, take them into their classrooms, and then reflect on how to refine them. The result, over time, is steady improvement, at the individual and community level.

Akihiko Takahashi has been at the heart of TTP from its very beginnings in Japan, first as a master teacher (he taught a lesson with students on stage and more than 1000 teachers in the audience, as part of a national teaching demonstration!), and then as a researcher and coach, helping to build the Japanese infrastructure for TTP. In this volume, he brings the central ideas of TTP to Western readers. If you've wondered why Japanese teachers and students do so well at mathematics, this book will show you why and show you how. Teaching Through Problem-solving gets students deeply involved in mathematics, making sense of it rather than simply following rules; when math makes sense in these ways, students understand it and can use it. This book shows what curricular tasks that support TTP look like, and it shows how you and your colleagues can use these ideas to enhance your teaching.

Alan Schoenfeld
Berkeley, CA
September 2020

Preface

I began my work supporting U.S. mathematics teachers in the 2000s, and since then I have had the privilege of visiting and observing mathematics classrooms in more than twenty states as well as in several countries throughout Africa, Asia, Europe, the Middle East, and North and South America. What I have learned from these visits is that teaching mathematics is not easy for many teachers, especially when it comes to engaging students in problem-solving. Although the national standards and curricula in all the places I visited emphasize the importance of nurturing students to think mathematically and solve problems on their own, teachers hesitate to allow students to think by themselves. I have heard them tell their students, "If you follow my instructions, you don't have to think. You can just plug in numbers and get the answers."

When *The Teaching Gap: Best Ideas From the World's Teachers for Improving Education in the Classroom* (Stigler & Hiebert, 1999) was published, I was surprised that the authors argued that Japanese mathematics lessons apply more reform ideas than typical U.S. lessons. They specifically point to the Japanese pedagogy based on reform ideas known as *Mondai Kaketsu Gakushuu*, or "Teaching Through Problem-Solving (TTP)." However, The National Council of Teachers of Mathematics had released standards and resources that reflected reform ideas (1980, 1989, 1991) years before the publication of *The Teaching Gap*. Therefore, Japanese teachers, including myself, had assumed most U.S. classrooms were applying these ideas by incorporating problem-solving in everyday lessons.

When I became a novice teacher, it was not easy for me to teach mathematics through problem-solving. My experience as a student was that of a traditional mathematics classroom: the teacher demonstrated how to get answers, and we, the students, imitated these demonstrations to complete exercises. In the beginning of my teaching career, my mentors told me, "You want to lead, not demonstrate, and you only want to use one good problem per 45-minute lesson." It was not easy for me to come up with good problems that would engage elementary students in mathematical discussion. I struggled to teach mathematics using this method.

Fortunately, I had the opportunity to join a volunteer discussion group of enthusiastic teachers from nearby schools. We met once a month after school to share ideas on how to use problem-solving in our classrooms and give each other feedback on our lesson plans. I was inspired by the teachers in this group, and with their support I gradually became comfortable using the Teaching Through Problem-solving approach. I also regularly taught public lessons as part of our schools' Lesson Study, the main professional development program used in Japanese schools. The feedback other teachers gave me on these lessons was also a powerful learning experience for me. It took me about six years to become comfortable teaching mathematics through problem-solving in my own classroom, and I never would have achieved this without the strong support of both these formal and informal professional development opportunities.

Then, I moved to Setagaya Elementary School, a national elementary school affiliated with Tokyo Gakugei University. The faculty at Setagaya conducts practical research and provides professional development opportunities for local schools. During my time at this school, I learned how to help other schools implement Teaching Through Problem-solving and conduct Lesson Study. As a member of Setagaya's curriculum materials design team, I became much more adept at crafting curricula. I also mentored about ten student teachers a year. All this I did with the support of my colleagues, Takashi Nakamura and Shunji Kurosawa.

After coming to the U.S., I realized that my twenty years of experience in Japanese classrooms might be not so common in schools outside Japan. Many teachers have neither formal nor informal opportunities to work with their colleagues as a team to address issues and improve teaching and learning. There are no programs like Lesson Study, and few such volunteer groups like the one in which I participated. Of course, some excellent and enthusiastic teachers have perfected their teaching craft on their own. However, most teachers need regular support to overcome challenges and try new ideas in their classrooms, just as I did. For the past twenty years, I have used my experience to help teachers implement Teaching Through Problem-solving in their schools by using Lesson Study. I have been fortunate to work with educators in the U.S. as well as other countries, including the U.K., Singapore, Thailand, Qatar, and Ireland. I wrote this book based on this work.

This book consists of four chapters. In Chapter 1, "Development and Major Concepts of Japanese 'Teaching Through Problem-Solving' (TTP)," I discuss how Japanese teachers and schools worked together to develop and popularize Teaching Through Problem-solving (TTP). To introduce how you can design and teach your own TTP lessons, I posit that there are three kinds of TTP lessons and four types of whole class discussion (*Neriage*) which feature in these lessons.

Chapter 2, "TTP Lessons You Can Use," provides a variety of example TTP lessons you can use in your own classroom, with several examples for each type of TTP. Chapter 3, "Designing Your Own TTP Lessons," was written as a guide for how teachers can start incorporating these lessons into their own classes. I also propose the use of *Neriage* Maps, sketches that can help you visualize the structure of *Neriage* in your lesson plans to illustrate how to facilitate your own whole class discussions. Chapter 4, "How TTP and Collaborative Lesson Research (CLR) Can Change Your School," discusses how the professional development program *Jyugyou Kenkyuu*, also known as "Lesson Study," has been helping Japanese teachers work together to develop and examine TTP lessons. I share Collaborative Lesson Research, a version of *Jyugyou Kenkyuu* that I developed for teachers outside of Japan, in the hope that it can help you adapt and expand TTP at your own school.

This book is based on my years of experience supporting teachers both in and outside of Japan. I hope the approaches proposed in these chapters help you use TTP lessons in your classroom. The best way to support your students to become independent problem-solvers is for you, the teacher, to enjoy solving interesting problems and sharing your ideas for problem-solving lessons with your colleagues. I hope you enjoy the TTP examples in this book, and that they help you begin your TTP journey by sharing your joy with your students.

References

National Council of Teachers of Mathematics. (1980). *An Agenda for Action: Recommendations for School Mathematics of the 1980s*. Reston, VA: National Council of Teachers of Mathematics.

National Council of Teachers of Mathematics. (1989). *Curriculum and Evaluation Standards for School Mathematics*. Reston, VA: National Council of Teachers of Mathematics.

National Council of Teachers of Mathematics. (1991). *Professional Standards for the Teaching of Mathematics*. Reston, VA: National Council of Teachers of Mathematics.

Stigler, J., & Hiebert, J. (1999). *The Teaching Gap: Best Ideas from the World's Teachers for Improving Education in the Classroom*. New York: Free Press.

1 Development and Major Concepts of Japanese "Teaching Through Problem-Solving" (TTP)

The unique Japanese pedagogical approach revealed in the publication of *The Teaching Gap: Best Ideas from the World's Teachers for Improving Education in the Classroom* caught the attention of teachers and researchers around the world (Stigler & Hiebert, 1999). Its video analysis of Japanese mathematics classrooms showed how Japanese teachers teach new mathematical concepts by giving students compelling mathematical challenges to solve on their own and discuss. Researchers found that this progressive approach, called "Teaching Through Problem-solving" (Schroeder & Lester, 1989), or "Structured Problem-solving" (Stigler & Hiebert, 1999), not only differed from typical U.S. classrooms but from other Asian classrooms as well (Mullis, 2000; Stigler & Hiebert, 1999). How did Japanese educators come up with such a unique method? How did it spread throughout Japan as a major approach to teaching mathematics?

In this book, I will share my insights based on decades of being front and center in Japan's education reform movement and the development of Teaching Through Problem-solving (TTP). My career has focused heavily on the promotion of TTP through research and personal practice. I have observed hundreds of lessons taught by fellow educators and spent years hosting public lessons and creating lesson plans. I have written this book based on my experience to show how teachers and schools outside Japan can use this approach to nurture their own students to become independent problem-solvers. This chapter will discuss the characteristics of TTP and outline how it became an established pedagogical practice in Japan.

1.1 The Need to Move Beyond the Lecture Method

1.1.1 The Purpose of the Study of Mathematics

Why do we have children study math? The most critical value of studying mathematics is to learn the process of mathematics, such as mathematical thinking and problem-solving. Viewing the world through a lens of mathematics gives young learners the chance to explore and make sense of the world around them. However, asking students to simply memorize facts and procedures, the results of others' exploration and discovery, makes mathematics dreary. How can we teach students how to grapple and engage with problems using mathematical reasoning if we only give them the opportunity to memorize formulas and facts?

We must teach students how to think mathematically. In 1998, the National Research Council in the United States put together a committee to synthesize a wide variety of research on mathematics education. Their report, *Adding it Up: Helping Children Learn Mathematics*, begins with a strong statement, "All young Americans must learn to think mathematically, and they must think mathematically to learn" (National Research Council, 2001, p. 1). Facts and procedures are essential, but students must learn how to think mathematically to solve problems. *Adding it Up* breaks down what it means to think mathematically into several different strands of proficiency (2001). These abilities are described as five interwoven and interdependent strands (Figure 1.1.01). The report defines them as:

- *conceptual understanding*—comprehension of mathematical concepts, operations, and relations
- *procedural fluency*—skill in carrying out procedures flexibly, accurately, efficiently, and appropriately
- *strategic competence*—ability to formulate, represent, and solve mathematical problems
- *adaptive reasoning*—capacity for logical thought, reflection, explanation, and justification
- *productive disposition*—habitual inclination to see mathematics as sensible, useful, and worthwhile, coupled with a belief in diligence and one's own efficacy.

(National Research Council, 2001, p. 116)

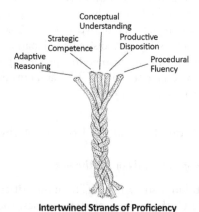

Intertwined Strands of Proficiency

Figure 1.1.01 Intertwined strands of proficiency.

Reprint of National Research Council (2001, p. 117)

However, the lecture method and routine repetition cannot nurture all five strands of proficiency.

Today's teachers will be familiar with the current Common Core State Standards (CCSS), which emphasize the need for students to learn how to think mathematically. They outline eight Standards for Mathematical Practice (MP):

- MP1 Make sense of problems and persevere in solving them.
- MP2 Reason abstractly and quantitatively.
- MP3 Construct viable arguments and critique the reasoning of others.
- MP4 Model with mathematics.
- MP5 Use appropriate tools strategically.
- MP6 Attend to precision.
- MP7 Look for and make use of structure.
- MP8 Look for and express regularity in repeated reasoning.

(Common Core State Standards Initiative, 2010, pp. 6–8)

However, these are demanding expectations which many schools and teachers are still not sure how to accomplish in their classrooms. Helping students develop mathematical thinking skills requires highly developed pedagogical strategies.

1.1.2 Problem-Solving as an Ideal Approach for Studying Mathematics

Research shows that giving students the opportunity to solve new problems on their own can help them achieve the demanding mathematical practice standards outlined by the CCSS. The National Council of Teachers of Mathematics emphasizes the importance of "building new mathematical knowledge through problem-solving" and defines problem-solving as "engaging in a task for which the solution method is not known in advance" (2000, p. 52). They argue that students should think mathematically to learn by solving novel problems in order to acquire knowledge of mathematical procedures. Independent problem-solving needs to be an integral part of all mathematics learning and not just an end of chapter activity.

Problem-solving has been a major focus of school mathematics education research for decades. Researchers corroborate that it's better for students to learn new mathematical concepts by trying to solve problems on their own rather than by just imitating the work of others. For example, in 1945, Polya suggested in his famous book *How to Solve It* that teachers should help students discreetly and unobtrusively as they work independently to solve new problems (Polya, 1945). In 1970, Gattegno, the inventor of geoboards and largely responsible for the popularity of Cuisenaire rods, argued that teachers cannot simply impart their knowledge to students through the lecture method (Gattegno, 1970). According to Lesh and Zawojewski (2007) the *Journal for*

Research in Mathematics and *Educational Study in Mathematics* published one hundred and fifty-six research articles on problem-solving during the 1980s and 1990s. These articles addressed topics such as studies on how students think mathematically when grappling with new problems and how to nurture them to develop their problem-solving skills (e.g., Schoenfeld, 1985). In 1980, the NCTM proposed in *Agenda for Action* that problem-solving should be the focus of school mathematics for everyone, researchers as well as teachers and educators (National Council of Teachers of Mathematics, 1980). Researchers and experts agree that students need to explore new mathematical concepts through problem-solving in order to develop the ability to think mathematically.

1.1.3 Challenges

However, despite recognizing the need to teach students how to think mathematically, there have been challenges in meeting this goal. International studies, such as the Trends in International Mathematics and Science Study (TIMSS), evaluate student achievement through the lens of Travers and Westbury's (1989) three aspects of curriculum: "intended curriculum," "implemented curriculum," and "attained curriculum" (Mullis, Martin, & Loveless, 2016; Travers, 2011; Travers & Westbury, 1989). The "intended curriculum" are the formal documents that describe what the students are expected to learn, such as CCSS and NCTM standards. The "implemented curriculum" are the lessons taught by a teacher. The "attained curriculum" is what the students actually learned (International Bureau of Education, 1995). Textbooks and other resources serve as potential curricula (e.g., Schmidt, McKnight, Valverde, Houang, & Wiley, 1997). They are designed to address the intended curriculum, but effective implementation relies on the skills of the teacher (Figure 1.1.02). This is why the lecture method, or simply "teaching the textbook," cannot successfully impart the intended curriculum by contemporary standards.

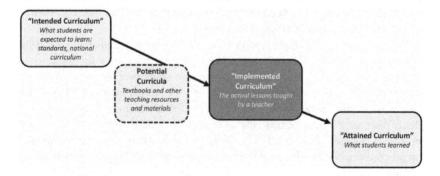

Figure 1.1.02 How effective curriculum implementation comes from the teacher. The three aspects of curriculum come from Travers and Westbury (1989).

The best way to ensure that the attained curriculum matches the intended curriculum has been the subject of much research. There is a significant amount of curricula available designed to teach students how to think mathematically. For example, the NCTM developed many guidelines and resources (e.g., National Council of Teachers of Mathematics, 1989, 2000). There are also several projects funded by the National Science Foundation, such as *Everyday Mathematics* developed by the University of Chicago School Mathematics Project (1992) and *The Connected Mathematics (CMP)* developed by Michigan State University (1996).

Still, the results have been uneven. Stigler and Hiebert (2009) argue there is no evidence that there was any improvement in teaching mathematics in the United States between 1995 and 1999. In 2018, Banilower et al. (2018) reported that more than 85% of teachers believed that students should learn mathematics by solving problems on their own and that students should also be able to explain their solutions. However, most American teachers do not give students such opportunities on a daily basis. Less than a quarter of classrooms make independent problem-solving and discussion a part of their everyday lessons (Banilower et al., 2018). It is still the exception and not the norm. As a result, student learning isn't meeting expectations (e.g., Mullis, Martin, & Loveless, 2016).

Teachers may be hesitant to switch their teaching methods. Leaving behind the lecture method requires a sophisticated pedagogical approach, which takes time to learn. Research shows that teachers may continue to rely on the lecture method due to a lack of professional development opportunities which would give them the chance to update their pedagogical skills (e.g., Stigler & Hiebert, 2009; Wei, Darling-Hammond, Andree, Richardson, & Orphanos, 2009). This struggle to shift to student-centered instruction doesn't only exist in the United States. Many countries whose curriculum emphasizes the importance of teaching students how to think mathematically are also grappling with how to implement these values into their classrooms. A gap remains between the intended and implemented curriculum. The Japanese pedagogical approach of TTP can help bridge this gap.

1.2 What is Japanese TTP?

1.2.1 The Development of TTP in Japan

Japanese educators and researchers have also spent decades focusing on how to nurture students' ability to think mathematically. Years of collaborative effort have produced a specialized pedagogical approach known as *Mondai Kaiketsu Gakushuu*, or "Teaching Through Problem-solving (TTP)." In TTP, teachers introduce new mathematical concepts by giving students new problems to try to solve on their own. The teacher doesn't act as a lecturer, but instead observes students as they work independently and facilitates a whole class discussion of their solution approaches. Asking students to wrestle directly with

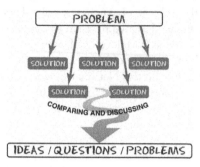

Figure 1.2.01 Comparing and discussing solution approaches during *Neriage*.
Reprinted from Takahashi (1996)

new concepts in this way imparts the mathematical thinking skills they need to become active learners. I discuss this in more detail in "The TTP Classroom" in this chapter.

TTP is the culmination of a major education reform movement in Japan. In 1958, the Japanese national curriculum introduced a new term, "mathematical thinking," in order to highlight its importance. To meet the challenge of teaching mathematical thinking, Japanese educators conducted various research projects and piloted new kinds of curricula designed to foster mathematical thinking and problem-solving skills. They also studied other countries' approaches. Translations of books such as Polya's *How to Solve It* (1954) and Charles and Lester's *Teaching Problem-solving: What, Why, and How* (1983) became very popular. And other volumes such as the NCTM's *An Agenda for Action* (National Council of Teachers of Mathematics, 1980) weren't formally published in the Japanese language but were made available in translation and circulated among teachers and researchers. Japanese educators studied these texts and worked together to come up with new pedagogical approaches and lesson plans in order to implement their ambitious ideas.

A project led by Shigeru Shimada pointed out a limitation of typical textbooks: most problems have only a single correct answer (Shimada, 1977). These single answer problems are used to introduce a particular solution approach. However, Shimada showed that if teachers give students a problem with multiple correct solutions, the students are more likely to discuss how to come up with an answer rather than just what the answer is. This approach, referred to as the "open-ended approach," became a popular way to help students learn how to derive solutions and to evaluate if their ideas make sense. I will discuss the open-ended approach in more detail with four example lessons in "TTP Lessons with Multiple Correct Solutions" in Chapter 2.

The reform movement resulted in a shift in the focus of Japanese mathematics education. The national curriculum, which has undergone a major revision about every ten years since World War II, reflected these new values. The 1989 national curriculum specifically stipulated that the purpose of teaching mathematics is to nurture students' mathematical thinking (Ministry of Education Japan, 1989a). For example, it states that the main objective of teaching how to find the areas of triangles and parallelograms in fifth grade is to nurture student's mathematical thinking by asking students to use what they have already learned about the area of more basic shapes to derive the formulas (Ministry of Education Japan, 1989a, p. 138). This instructs teachers to guide students' independent investigations to help them develop mathematical thinking skills. It acknowledges the need for TTP. By the 1990s, TTP became the main pedagogical approach for teaching mathematics across Japan in most elementary schools as well as in some lower secondary schools.

1.2.2 Neriage, *the Heart of TTP*

TTP has several features that set it apart from other kinds of problem-solving lessons. One essential feature, the heart of TTP, is a dynamic and collaborative whole class discussion called *Neriage* (Shimizu, 1999). The teacher facilitates a *Neriage* discussion to look back on students' solution approaches to help them derive the essential facts, concepts, and procedures (Figure 1.2.01). In typical non-TTP problem-solving lessons the goal is just to solve the problem, not to explore any new mathematical concepts. Students share their solutions as if they are doing a show and tell activity, but they don't learn anything new (Takahashi, 2008). However, in TTP lessons which feature *Neriage*, students discover and explore new mathematical concepts and procedures. The term *Neriage* has been widely used among Japanese teachers and researchers of mathematics education since the 1980s. This feature of TTP is key to maximizing student learning of mathematical concepts and procedures, as well as their ability to think mathematically. I will discuss *Neriage* in more detail in "The TTP Classroom," in this chapter. I will also outline the four major types of *Neriage* in section 1.5, "The Four Kinds of Whole Class Discussions (*Neriage*) in TTP" and provide a TTP lesson example for each type.

1.2.3 *TTP is an Advanced Pedagogy*

TTP is an advanced pedagogical approach. Sugiyama (2008) explains three different levels of teaching mathematics. He writes that a "Level 1" teacher can demonstrate essential mathematics such as facts, concepts, procedures, and practices, a "Level 2" teacher can explain the meaning behind the essential mathematics, and a "Level 3" teacher can guide students to become independent learners who can discover essential mathematics (Suigyama, 2008). Level 1 and 2 are lecture method approaches to teaching. Level 3 embodies the TTP approach to leading a classroom.

A Level 2 teacher has mathematical pedagogy skills that a Level 1 teacher doesn't. They can explain the mathematical reasoning behind concepts and procedures (e.g., Ball, Thames, & Phelps, 2008; Ma, 1999). For example, a lesson on the multiplication of two two-digit numbers, such as 12 × 23 (Figure 1.2.02), is very different when taught at Level 1 then when it is taught at Level 2. A Level 1 teacher can show how to multiply 12 times 23 step by step and let students imitate the process. However, students may not understand why they have to multiply single-digit numbers four times (3 × 2, 3 × 1, 2 × 2, and 2 × 1) because if they were going to add 12 and 23 they would only add single-digit numbers twice (2 + 3 and 1 + 2). A Level 1 teacher may dismiss questions, saying, "You'll get it after you practice it enough." However, a Level 2 teacher can use diagrams or models to help explain why.

However, Level 3, the level needed for successful TTP lessons, requires an even higher level of pedagogical ability. Level 3 teachers must carefully design lessons so students can discover new ideas and procedures by themselves. In the case of multiplying two two-digit numbers, a TTP teacher will craft a lesson in which students can discover through their own independent exploration that they can calculate the multiplication of two two-digit numbers by performing single-digit multiplication four times. Because the students must be able to solve it on their own, the teacher has to find a problem that is not too challenging. They must also be able to support students when they are struggling while not explaining the reasoning outright. One clear way that Level 3 TTP teaching differs from Level 1 and 2 is that the teacher may not

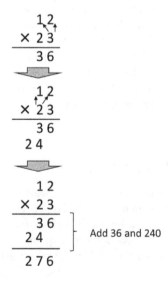

Figure 1.2.02 Multiplication of a two-digit number by a two-digit number.

spend the majority of the class time explaining or demonstrating. However, while the teacher may not talk much during the lesson itself, they must spend lots of time carefully planning the lesson and anticipating students' responses in order to successfully engage them during class.

1.2.4 TTP is the Product of Lesson Study

TTP lessons were refined over time. This is due to the fact that unlike other countries, Japan already had an established professional development practice in which teachers collaborate to develop a specific plan for a lesson, teach students based on the plan, and discuss its impacts on the student learning based on the observation of the lesson. This practice is called *Jyugyou Kenkyuu,* or "Lesson Study." The collaboration and dedication to research in schools' regular Lesson Study practices helped Japanese educators develop and share effective TTP practices. Japanese teachers have been practicing Lesson Study since the early 1900s, the beginning of public education (Makinae, 2019). When Lesson Study was introduced to the outside world by U.S. researchers (e.g., Lewis & Tsuchida, 1998; Stigler & Hiebert, 1999; Yoshida, 1999), readers saw it as a powerful professional development program. However, Lesson Study is more than just the sharing of new ideas, it is also the opportunity to develop new ones. Education researchers, teachers, curriculum designers, and textbook publishers work together to create new pedagogical ideas, curriculum materials, and mathematical tasks through Lesson Study.

Teachers are able to choose and adapt the right problems for effective TTP classes because of the work done in Lesson Study. Japanese TTP lessons generally spend the entire class time, forty-five minutes for elementary grades and fifty minutes for lower secondary grades, exploring one carefully designed problem. The effectiveness of a TTP lesson hinges on the richness of this chosen problem. During Lesson Study, teachers conduct an in-depth study of the mathematics and curricula material related to the objective of the lesson. They must also anticipate students' possible responses to the problem, including misconceptions and incorrect solutions, in order to plan how to address them during *Neriage*. This extensive preparation helps teachers choose the best problems to use in their lessons.

The practice of Lesson Study also satisfies recommendations made by American education researchers. As shown in the instructional triangle created by the National Research Council (Figure 1.2.03), teachers must consider the students' prior learning in order to choose an appropriately challenging problem that will accomplish the objective of the lesson. Lesson Study provides a structure for accomplishing this. I will discuss the process of Lesson Study in more detail and how you can use it in your schools in Chapter 3 "Designing Your Own TTP Lessons" and in Chapter 4 "How TTP and Collaborative Lesson Research Can Change Your School."

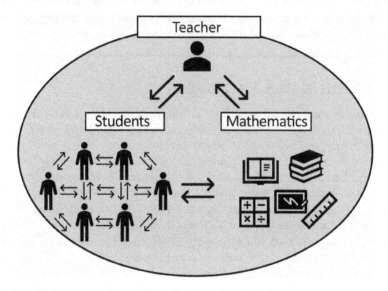

Figure 1.2.03 Instructional triangle.

Adapted from *Adding it Up: Helping Children Learn Mathematics* (National Research Council, 2001, p. 314)

1.2.5 *The Importance of Writing*

Another characteristic of TTP is the focus on writing. It is critical to nurture students' ability to represent their ideas using diagrams, mathematical expressions, tables, graphs, and sentences. Japanese teachers carefully plan how they will write on the board during *Neriage* to support student discussion. What is written on the board will also serve as the model which students can record in their notebooks. Writing in notebooks at the end of each lesson is seen as a critical activity to help students become independent problem solvers. I discuss this in more detail in "The TTP Classroom" in this chapter.

1.3 Progression of TTP in Japan

1.3.1 *Evolution of the TTP Lesson Structure*

During the early stages of developing TTP in Japan in the 1970s and early 1980s, many schools and teachers started using the four phases of problem-solving by Polya (1945) as a framework to design lessons. These four phases are: understand the problem, devise a plan, carry out the plan, and look back at your work (Figure 1.3.01). However, TTP lessons moved beyond Polya's four phases as their structure evolved over time.

1. Understand the problem
2. Devise a plan
3. Carry out the plan
4. Look back on your work

Figure 1.3.01 Polya's four phases of problem-solving.

Adapted from *How to Solve It: A New Aspect of Mathematical Method* (Polya, 1945)

   Stigler and Hiebert (1999) noted that Japanese mathematics lessons typically followed a similar progression. First, they look back on the previous lesson, then they present the problem for the day, then students work individually or in groups, followed by a discussion of solution methods, and finally the class highlights and summarizes the major points (Stigler & Hiebert, 1999). Similar descriptions of Japanese TTP lessons are given in the proceedings of the US-Japan Seminar of Mathematical Problem-solving (Becker & Miwa, 1987; Becker, Silver, Kantowski, Travers, & Wilson, 1990). Hashimoto also writes that this type of instruction had been promoted widely throughout Japan since 1978; they cite a hundred such examples from 1986 ranging from first to twelfth grade classes (Becker & Miwa, 1987, p. 113). This structure is very similar to the one used in Japanese TTP classrooms today.

   The progression of TTP lessons from Polya's four phases to this current structure is the result of decades of education research of which I myself was a part. Over the course of my involvement in the development of TTP, I have identified the evolution of the structure of TTP lessons through the years. Although most TTP lessons shared a common approach, the structure of the lessons changed slightly in response to insights gained through extensive research and practice. I have categorized and labeled these different Japanese TTP lesson structures as Types A, B, C, and D (Figure 1.3.02).

   In the 1970s and early 1980s, the early years of using problem-solving in the mathematics classroom, I most commonly saw Type A lessons. The Type A structure follows Polya's four phases exactly. Type A began to shift to Type B during the 1980s. Sakamoto Elementary School, a leading school of mathematics education reform in Tokyo, published a book based on their schoolwide Lesson Study in 1983. The book references Polya's four phases, but they ended up combining "devise a plan" and "carry out the plan" into a single activity as shown in Type B (Figure 1.3.02). They reported that while older students may be able to devise a plan before testing it out, elementary level students struggled with this task. Therefore, they combined the two phases into "devise and carry out a plan." This modification valued primary school children's independent exploration while better nurturing them as problem solvers. After the publication of Sakamoto Elementary's book, Type B lessons became a popular style in Japanese classrooms. "Devise and carry out

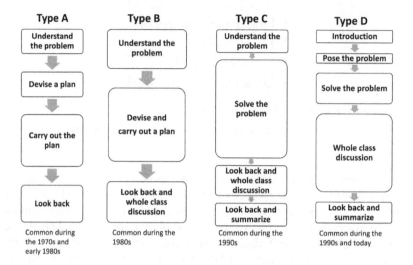

Figure 1.3.02 Evolution of the Japanese TTP lesson structure.

Note: One class period is 45 minutes long.

a plan" was gradually replaced with "solve the problem," in Type C lessons (Figure 1.3.02), which became more common during the 1990s. "Solve the problem" was also a much longer activity than "devise and carry out a plan," giving more time to students to work independently.

However, some experienced elementary mathematics teachers began to argue that the whole class discussion should be the main focal point of TTP lessons, as shown in Type D (Figure 1.3.02). For example, a nation-wide study group, *Sansuu Jyugyou Kenkyuukai* [Mathematics Lesson Study Group], published a collection of lesson plan ideas (1994). They argued that lessons should focus more on class discussion as a space to examine each student's approach and learn something new. By prioritizing the whole class discussion, Type D lessons better help students develop mathematical thinking, the main objective of TTP lessons. Japanese teachers often say that finding the answer is not the main goal of TTP lessons. Rather, it is for students to learn by both solving and examining their solution approaches. The real mathematics learning happens after students try to solve the problem. Type D is the structure most commonly used in TTP lessons today.

The following outlines the typical structure of a contemporary TTP lesson in Japan, based on my observations:

- Introduction (about 3–5 min)

    - Prepare students for the day's lesson, look back on what they learned in the previous lesson.

- Posing the problem (about 5–7 min)

  - Present the problem.
  - If necessary, support students as they share what ideas or previous learning may be used to solve the problem.

- Student problem-solving (about 7–10 min)

  - Take note of student responses to prepare for *Neriage*, the whole class discussion.

- Comparison and discussion (about 20–25 min)

  - Facilitate *Neriage*, let students share their solutions and guide discussion so that the class understands the math involved in the lesson.

- Summarizing (about 5–10 min)

  - Help students summarize the main ideas of the lesson.
  - Let each student record notes on the lesson, including individual reflections.

1.3.2 The Evolution of TTP's Influence on Japanese Mathematics Textbooks

I have already mentioned the Japanese professional development practice of Lesson Study as one of the main reasons Japanese educators were able to work together to refine TTP lessons. Following the innovations to TTP developed through Lesson Study, Japanese textbooks reflected a gradual shift from Level 2 teaching, the lecture method, to Level 3 teaching, supporting students as they develop strategies to solve new problems (Watanabe, 2014). To demonstrate this, I have translated several editions of a widely used elementary Japanese mathematics textbook to show how a particular unit changed over time.

Tokyo Shoseki published a government authorized textbook in 1954 (Iyanaga, 1954). I have reproduced four pages from the unit, which introduces how to find the area of rectangles and squares (Figure 1.3.03). The title of the unit is "The Class Garden." Page 26 shows an image of students working in a garden on the school grounds (Figure 1.3.03). Below this image it reads:

> Yoshiko's class will be working on their class gardens. To make sure everyone in the class does the same amount of work in the gardens, they need to divide up the spaces equally. Let's learn how to measure the size of things like land or buildings. Let's also learn how to do multiplication to calculate those measurements.
>
> (Iyanaga, 1954, p. 26; my translation)

Page 27, titled "The areas of the gardens," explains:

> Yoshiko's class has two gardens, one in front of the school and another alongside the building. The one in front of the school is a rectangle that is 5 meters long and 3 meters wide. The one alongside the building is a 4 meter long and 4 meter wide square. The class is discussing which one is bigger. Yoshiko says, "Why don't we divide the length and the width of each garden into 1 meter sections, and see how many squares with 1 meter sides each of the gardens has?"
>
> (Iyanaga, 1954, p. 27; my translation)

Two questions are posed at the bottom of the page:

1   How many squares with 1 m sides do the above rectangle and square each have?
2   How can we quickly figure out how many squares there are?

(Iyanaga, 1954, p. 28; my translation)

Page 28 formally introduces the mathematical term "area" and "1 m²" as a unit of measurement. It also introduces the formulas for finding the area of

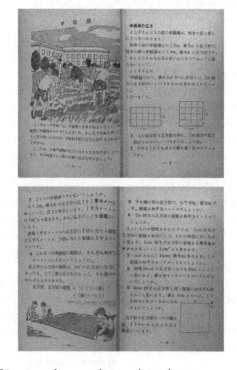

Figure 1.3.03 1954 unit on the area of rectangles and squares.

Reprinted with permission from *Atarashii Sansuu* [*New Mathematics*] (Iyanaga, 1954, pp. 26–29)

rectangles and squares. The following page, page 29, gives students the chance to practice calculating the area of rectangles and squares using the formula and also introduces a new unit of measurement, 1 cm^2. This 1954 textbook introduces the concept and the procedure for measuring area in three pages, pages 26–28, and includes some additional exercises on page 29. It introduces how to measure area in an everyday context familiar to students. However, it does not discuss why it's helpful to use small squares to compare the size of the spaces and why we use multiplication.

The Japanese national curriculum was revised in 1958, and this unit was changed from a fifth grade topic to a fourth grade one (Ministry of Education Japan, 1958). After this revision, there was a movement to modernize mathematics education to address mathematical thinking, specifically paying attention to the creative process (Nakashima, 1997). As a result, this area unit began to include more hands-on activities in updated editions to help students discover and understand the concepts on their own.

In the 1976 edition of this unit (Iyanaga, 1976), the area formula isn't formally introduced until the fifth page, two pages later than in the 1954 textbook (Figure 1.3.04). This is due to the inclusion of several new hands-on activities which explore the usefulness of using unit squares to compare sizes. The first page, page 120, introduces the term "area" and shows how different shapes can have the same area by displaying three different figures, each made up of six squares (Figure 1.3.04). Page 121 asks students to copy two shapes, a rectangle and a square, onto paper, and then cut them out and overlap them to compare the sizes. Page 122 begins by asking students to determine how many squares with 1 cm sides can fit into the rectangle and the square, respectively. Then, it introduces "1 cm^2" as a unit of area measurement. The following page, page 123, asks students to find out how many unit squares, 1 cm^2, can fit into a new pair of rectangles. The formula for finding area isn't introduced until the following page, page 124 (Iyanaga, 1976). A teacher may spend two to three 45-minute periods on this unit because these lessons expect students to conduct several hands-on investigations. The 1976 edition of Iyanaga is quite different from the 1954 Iyanaga edition.

A notable change from the previous editions happened in the 1992 edition of the textbook (Maehara & Sugiyama, 1992) (Figure 1.3.05). This edition was the first one released after the national curriculum was changed in 1989 (Ministry of Education Japan, 1989b). The revised 1989 national curriculum dictated that problem-solving should be frequently addressed in order to provide students opportunities to think by themselves. It stated that it is crucial to provide children with the opportunity to think and solve problems based on what they have learned, and that it is important to provide activities that include concrete manipulations, thought experiments, etc. (Ministry of Education Japan, 1989b). As a result, the unit on finding the area of squares and rectangles in the 1992 edition includes even more discovery activities and doesn't introduce the area formula until the sixth page (Maehara & Sugiyama, 1992). This is in stark contrast with the 1954 edition, which presented the formula on the third page of the unit.

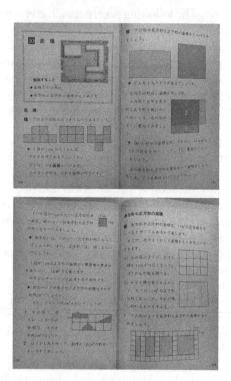

Figure 1.3.04 1976 unit on the area of rectangles and squares.

Reprinted with permission from *Atarashii Sansuu* [*New Mathematics*] (Iyanaga, 1976, pp. 120–123)

The first page of area unit in the 1992 edition is on the right hand side, unlike any of the earlier editions (Figure 1.3.05). This is so the problem can be posed without students seeing any hints about how to solve it. I have reproduced this page with my translations and notes (Figure 1.3.06). It shows two flower beds and asks students how can they figure out which one is larger. However, the students will not see any methods until they flip to the next page. Unlike any of the previous editions, students are encouraged to attack this problem by themselves without seeing any guidance. This is the first textbook that uses a TTP lesson to open the unit.

Despite the many changes to the unit over the years, the main problem itself, comparing the area of a 3 × 5 rectangle with a 4 × 4 square, has remained unchanged since 1954. It was the approach for investigating this concept which changed radically over time. As we look back on the trajectory of mathematics teaching and learning, it is clear that TTP was not one person's idea or innovation. TTP has been shaped by years of tireless effort by Japanese mathematics education researchers, classroom teachers, school administrators, policymakers, and textbook editors and publishers.

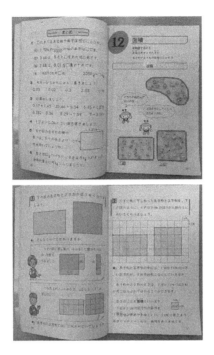

Figure 1.3.05 1992 unit on the area of rectangles and squares.

Reprinted with permission from *Atarashii Sansuu* [*New Mathematics*] (Maehara & Sugiyama, 1992, pp. 22–25)

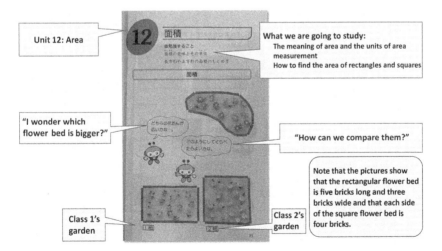

Figure 1.3.06 The first page of the 1992 unit on the area of rectangles and squares with my translations and notes.

Adapted with permission from *Atarashii Sansuu* [*New Mathematics*] (Maehara & Sugiyama, 1992, p. 23)

1.4 The TTP Classroom

1.4.1 A Research Lesson I Observed

I observed a lesson, as a part of a district-wide Lesson Study in 1979, when I was a novice teacher at a public school in Tokyo. It was hosted at another public school in the same district and taught by a second-year teacher who worked there. This teacher and her team developed a lesson that introduced a new mathematics topic to her third-grade class by creating a problematic classroom situation that the students then had to resolve.

The teacher began by telling her students that they were going to play a game:

Teacher (T):   Let's play a game of ring toss!
Students (S):   Yay, sounds fun!
T: Move all your desks and chairs to the back of the classroom so we can have enough space to play.

The students moved their desks and chairs and then stood in a group in the front half of the classroom. In the front half of the room there was a line of tape on the floor stretching straight across which the teacher had prepared prior to the lesson (Figure 1.4.01).

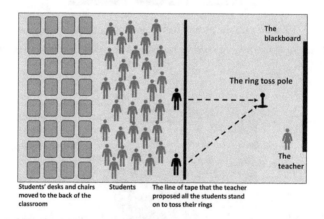

| Students' desks and chairs moved to the back of the classroom | Students | The line of tape that the teacher proposed all the students stand on to toss their rings |

Figure 1.4.01   How the classroom was arranged when teacher posed the problem during the ring toss research lesson.

T: Each of you will get a ring to throw. Everyone will line up on this line and then throw your rings all at the same time. Those whose rings land on the pole will be the winners!

As the students lined up, one student at the far end of the line started to complain:

S: Ms. [Teacher], I don't think it's fair that I have to throw my ring from all the way over here, everyone in the middle of the line is way closer to the pole.

Their classmates agreed:

S: Yeah, I think this line might be unfair.
T: Well, if this line isn't fair, what kind of line or shape do you think would make the game fair?
S: Maybe a "V" shape?
S: We could make a square around the pole?
T: Okay, let's come up with a better idea.

The teacher then wrote the problem on the board, "Think about how we can all stand side by side in order to make this ring toss game fair." Students had a short time to think on their own and then they discussed it in small groups. The teacher then initiated a classroom discussion of everyone's ideas. She had students draw their ideas on the blackboard under the problem she had written. They came up with several different ideas (Figure 1.4.02).

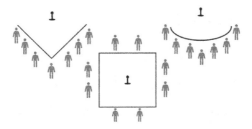

Figure 1.4.02 Some of the ideas the students came up with during the ring toss research lesson.

T: How did you come up with your ideas?
S: I tried to come up with a way that each of us would be the same distance from the pole.
T: Do you think if we line up using your ideas that all of you will be the same distance from the pole?
S: We can try and see.
S: We can use a piece of string to measure to make sure we are all the same distance from the pole.

The teacher asked a few volunteers to come stand around the pole to help her make the figures the students had drawn on the blackboard. Students began to realize that maybe they needed to make a circle so everyone could stand an equal distance from the pole.

S: It should be a circle!
T: Okay, let's use a piece of string to help us make sure everyone can stand an equal distance from the pole. Then we can play our ring toss game.

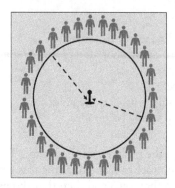

Figure 1.4.03 The solution students came up with at the end of the ring toss research lesson.

The teacher let the students make the shape.

T: Are you happy with this shape?
S: Yes, now we're all the same distance from the pole.
T: Do you know what we call this shape?

All the students said, "A circle."

T: Did you know that we could form a circle by making all the positions equally distant from the pole?
S: No, I thought that "circles" is just what we call round shapes.
T: Let's study more about circles. We can play our ring toss game during recess.

This concluded the lesson. I was impressed that the students came up with the definition of a circle on their own in order to make the ring toss game fair.

1.4.2 TTP as an Integral Part of the Mathematics Curriculum

I observed this lesson more than forty years ago. It was an innovative way to invite students to discover what a circle is. The concept behind this TTP lesson has since become part of contemporary government authorized textbooks in Japan.

As I discussed in section 1.3, Japanese teachers initially developed TTP lessons on their own, but many of the most successful lessons were later incorporated into official textbooks. The ring toss lesson I observed in 1979 is no exception. It has since been used in several textbooks over the years (e.g., Fujii & Majima, 2020a). One such textbook has been translated into English, titled *New Mathematics for Elementary School* (Fujii & Majima, 2020b). This third-grade textbook uses a version of the ring toss lesson as the opening lesson for the unit on circles (Figure 1.4.04).

Figure 1.4.04 Opening page of the unit on circles.

Reprinted with permission from *New mathematics for Elementary School 3A* (Fujii & Majima, 2020b, p. 121)

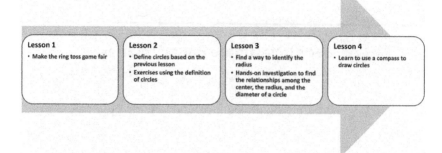

Figure 1.4.05 An outline of the four lessons in the unit on circles in *New Mathematics for Elementary School* (Fujii & Majima, 2020b). These lessons address Japan's national curriculum standards for third grade: to understand circles as a geometric figure and to understand the concepts of center, radius, and diameter.

The circle unit in *New Mathematics for Elementary School* is a series of TTP lessons (Figure 1.4.05). The second lesson asks students to construct several paths made up of points that are all an equal distance from a center point (Fujii & Majima, 2020b). After performing this task, the students will realize that all the paths they made look like circles. The third lesson asks students to find the radius of the circle without being given the location of the center (Figure 1.4.06). This hands-on investigation deepens students' understanding of a circle and helps them explore the relationships among the center, radius, and diameter. In this investigation, students trace a circle on a sheet of paper using an everyday object, such as a coffee mug. Students then cut out the circle and fold it in half to find the center, the diameter, and the radius. In the fourth lesson, they draw circles using a compass (Fujii & Majima, 2020b).

The four lessons in this unit use TTP lessons to address third grade mathematics standards. Each lesson invites students to engage in mathematics by solving everyday problems and performing hands-on activities. So while the development of Japanese TTP lessons historically began as isolated lessons, they are now an integral part of the curriculum. TTP lessons are recognized as the most effective way to help students acquire both mathematical knowledge and thinking skills.

1.4.3 Building a TTP Classroom

The instructional triangle (Figure 1.2.03) is crucial to building a TTP classroom. Each lesson is constructed with the relationships between mathematics, students, and teacher in mind. The teacher of a TTP classroom supports students as they actively engage in the process of mathematics. As I introduced in section 1.3, the structure of a modern TTP classroom can be broken down

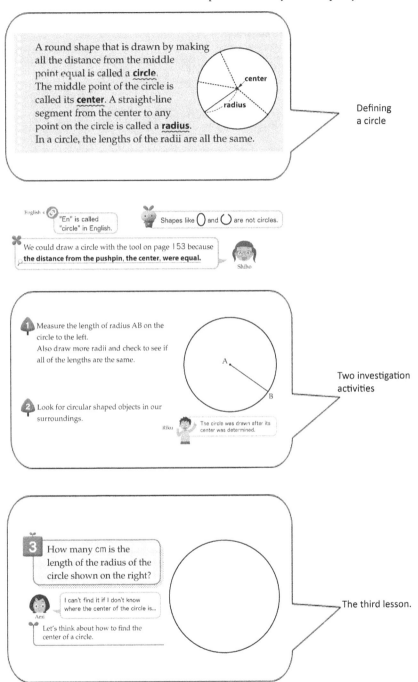

Figure 1.4.06 Excerpt from unit on circles with my notes.

Adapted with permission from *New mathematics for Elementary School* 3A (Fujii & Majima, 2020b, pg. 123)

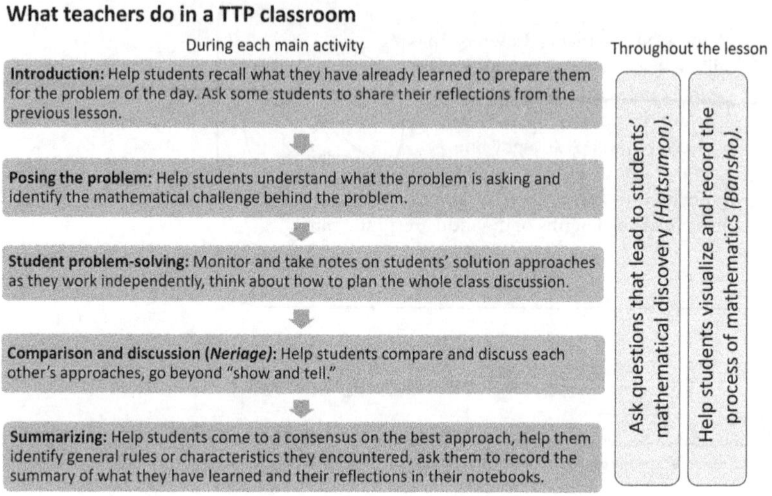

What teachers do in a TTP classroom

During each main activity   Throughout the lesson

Introduction: Help students recall what they have already learned to prepare them for the problem of the day. Ask some students to share their reflections from the previous lesson.

⬇

Posing the problem: Help students understand what the problem is asking and identify the mathematical challenge behind the problem.

⬇

Student problem-solving: Monitor and take notes on students' solution approaches as they work independently, think about how to plan the whole class discussion.

⬇

Comparison and discussion (*Neriage*): Help students compare and discuss each other's approaches, go beyond "show and tell."

⬇

Summarizing: Help students come to a consensus on the best approach, help them identify general rules or characteristics they encountered, ask them to record the summary of what they have learned and their reflections in their notebooks.

Ask questions that lead to students' mathematical discovery (*Hatsumon*).

Help students visualize and record the process of mathematics (*Bansho*).

Figure 1.4.07 Main components of TTP: What teachers do in a TTP classroom.

into five main activities: Introduction, Posing the problem, Student problem-solving, Comparison and discussion, and Summarizing (Figure 1.4.07). I will describe these and the other main components of TTP in detail.

Introduction: Looking Back on Previous Learning

People often say that learning mathematics is like building with blocks, each lesson should build upon the previous one. To connect previous learning to the next challenge, the teacher should allow students to look back on what they have already learned. To accomplish this, rather than giving a short lecture such as, "Do you remember what we did yesterday?" Japanese teachers will often invite their students to share their self-reflections from the previous lesson. This helps motivate the class to tackle the next challenge.

These self-reflections are usually written during the "summarizing" activity at the end of a lesson. Students often write what they have learned in these reflections, but also what they want to learn next. Teachers collect and read these on their own after class. They also provide a valuable opportunity to learn what the students who didn't speak during the lesson were thinking. Students' self-reflections can be a great source for formative assessment.

Posing the Problem: Help Students Grasp the Mathematical Challenge behind the Problem

A typical TTP lesson is structured around one main problem, so you must consider your class in order to choose a problem that will be appropriate. If the problem is too challenging and unrelated to what they have already learned, students may be unable to engage and give up. If the problem is too easy, they may not learn anything new. Teachers must consider not only the mathematics, but also how their students think and feel. For example, even if students in another classroom enjoyed a certain problem, that doesn't mean that your students will have the same learning experience. Successful TTP classrooms must always consider the instructional triangle (Figure 1.2.03), keeping in mind the relationship between the mathematics at hand and the students. Both formal and informal formative assessments are key when designing TTP lessons.

Once you have chosen a problem, you must decide the best way to present it in order to maximize student interest in solving it. The ring toss lesson I observed in 1979 sparked students' immediate engagement by giving them an unfair situation to resolve. It is more important to present why we are exploring a problem than just to explain what the problem is. You must communicate that the goal of the lesson is to grasp the mathematical challenge that the problem represents. Japanese teachers refer to the actual problem itself as *mondai* and the mathematical challenge it represents as *kadai*. For example, 35 + 12 could be the *mondai* of the day, however, the *kadai* behind that problem would be, "how can we calculate addition with larger numbers such as 35 + 12 without counting up one by one?" In order to help students understand the *kadai*, the Japanese teachers make sure to choose a problem that is similar to one that they have already studied, but requires the students to extend their previous learning. For example, 35 + 12 is an appropriate problem to use if students have already learned about single-digit addition and place value notation. The teacher can ask how 35 + 12 compares to other problems they have explored. Leading this kind of discussion when introducing the problem helps students identify the mathematical challenge behind it.

Student Problem-solving: Monitor Students as They Work Independently

While students work on the problem individually, the teacher walks around the TTP classroom to monitor how each student is trying to approach the problem. Japanese teachers often use a seating chart to jot down which students come up with what approach, or who is struggling with which part of the problem. It can help teachers guide students as they work and also help them plan an effective whole class discussion. Because this monitoring process is central to successful TTP lessons, Japanese teachers refer to it using the technical term *Kikan Jyunshi* or *Kikan Shido* (see Shimizu, 1999).

Monitoring students as they work has benefits in the moment. If a student is truly stuck, you can ask them some relevant leading questions to help them refocus. If many students seem to not understand the problem, you can take a moment to clarify what the problem is asking. Still, you may find that not every student is able to solve the problem. This is okay. It's important to let them wrestle with it on their own; this gives them a chance to at least identify what they already know and what they do not know. Furthermore, not only will they be able to come to understand the problem during the following whole class discussion, by sharing their struggles they can help deepen everyone's understanding of the topic.

The quality of the whole class discussion hinges on how well you can monitor students as they work independently. Teachers can use the information they gather during this time to plan who they want to call on during the whole class discussion, and in what sequence. Since these decisions need to be made quickly during class time, it's very helpful to consider your students' potential responses when planning the lesson so you can better anticipate and take note of their actual responses.

After the teacher takes notes on how each student is approaching the problem, they may want to let them work with partners or small groups before engaging in the whole class discussion. There are pros and cons of using this method. One advantage may be that students get a chance to practice explaining their ideas to their peers casually before the whole class discussion. However, Japanese educators have noticed that students who employed unique approaches will realize that their tactics were not popular and will not want to share their ideas during the whole class discussion. As a result, only the most popular ideas may end up being discussed during the whole class discussion. Still, the advantage of small groups may outweigh this risk as the practice gives students a chance to help each other understand how to solve the problem. Teachers need to keep the objective of the lesson and what they know about their students in mind when making these decisions.

Comparison and Discussion (Neriage): *Help Students Compare and Discuss Their Work*

Because the students will tackle the problem of the day in different ways, the TTP teacher must lead them to come up with a shared understanding of how to solve the problem, the *Mondai*, and the mathematical challenge behind it, the *Kadai*. If students only "show and tell" their work without engaging in any comparison or discussion, the class misses out on a critical learning opportunity. The real mathematical discussion begins after students share their solution approaches (Takahashi, 2008, 2011). Japanese teachers call this specific kind of mathematics classroom discussion *Neriage*, which I briefly introduced in section 1.2. Shimizu writes:

> *Neriage* describes the dynamic and collaborative nature of the whole class discussion . . . In Japanese, the term *Neriage* means kneading up or polishing up. In the context of teaching, the term works as a metaphor for the process of polishing students' ideas and of developing an integrated mathematical idea through the whole class discussion. Japanese teachers regard *Neriage* as critical for the success or failure of the lesson.
>
> (Shimizu, 1999, p. 110)

The ideas that each student comes up with while working on their own are great resources for the class to discuss. Stevenson (1980) reported that Japanese teachers valued each student's attempt to solve the problem, even if the answer was incorrect or incomplete. Each student's work can be thought of as a stone. If a stone is left as is, it may be rough and unattractive. However, if students can help each other polish their work, these stones can become precious treasures. This polishing up is what *Neriage* is all about.

Researchers have conducted several case studies over the years on *Neriage* in Japanese TTP classrooms (e.g., Fujii, 2016; Lewis & Tsuchida, 1998; Shimizu, 1999, 2003; Stigler & Hiebert, 1999; Takahashi, 2008; Watanabe, 2014; Yoshida, 1999). To engage the students in discussion, the teacher should be like the conductor of an orchestra, leading the students to help each other. Teachers should avoid explaining students' work to the class themselves. Instead, you can ask a student to explain their classmate's work. It is particularly beneficial if you ask them to explain an approach that that they did not use themselves. You can also invite students to ask questions about each other's work.

To maximize student interaction, your discussion plan needs to have a certain degree of flexibility and openness. A series of questions and answers between the teacher and students, such as, Teacher → Student → Teacher → Student, may be too stifling. Rather, an effective TTP class prioritizes discussion among the students, such as, Teacher → Student → Student → Student → Student. There are several popular types of *Neriage* typically employed in Japanese TTP. The teacher selects which one to use based on the topic of the lesson, the nature of the problem, and the lesson objective. The four main types of *Neriage* are as follows:

1   Address several different approaches to the problem in sequence, starting with the most basic and leading up to the most sophisticated in order to examine the progression of thought.
2   Compare different approaches side by side to help students find the relationships between them.
3   Contrast two approaches to highlight typical misconceptions and misunderstandings (debate).
4   Compare multiple different solutions using an open-ended problem to identify general rules or characteristics.

These structures are quite different from each other in terms of presentation, but they all are based on a flexible and open exchange of ideas. When the imagined ideal is a narrow path, we tend to not want to go another route, even when necessary. If a plan is too rigid and discussion veers toward an unexpected track, students and teacher may find themselves stuck. By allowing for multiple ways to the destination, the teacher can lead a productive student discussion and better guide them to conquer the mathematical challenge. I will discuss the above four major types of *Neriage* in more detail in section 1.5.

Summarizing: Lead a Student to Look Back on What They Learned

Researchers have recognized that Japanese teachers value the summary of the day's lesson much more than the typical American teacher (Becker & Miwa, 1987; Becker, Silver, Kantowski, Travers, & Wilson, 1990; Shimizu, 1999; Stevenson & Stigler, 1992; Stigler & Hiebert, 1999). Japanese teachers even have a specific term to describe this activity, "*Matome*" (see Bass, Usiskin, & Burrill, 2002, p. 253; Shimizu, 1999, p. 111). *Matome* typically consists of two parts: first, students look back and sum up what they learned that day in class, then they write it down in their notebooks along with their reflections.

During *Matome*, teachers can use what is written on the board to help students come to a shared understanding of the problem itself (the *Mondai*) as well as a consensus regarding the mathematical challenge behind it (the *Kadai*). Earlier, I gave the example of a *Mondai* of the day, 35 + 12, and the *Kadai* behind it, "how can we calculate addition of larger numbers like 35 + 12 without counting up one by one?" During *Matome* at the end of the lesson, the teacher can guide the class to look back over all their approaches for adding 35 and 12, what the correct answer was, and what strategy may be the most efficient. This is another way TTP discussions benefit from thoughtful and organized board writing. Students can realize that adding the tens together and the ones together may be much easier than counting up 12 one by one from 35. Thus, the solution to "how can we calculate addition of larger numbers?" can be, "when we add two two-digit numbers, we can add the tens together and the ones together." The teacher summarizes the students' discussion and writes this statement on the board as the summary of the day and lets each student copy it into their notebook.

After the class agrees on the summary statement, the teacher will often ask students to write reflections. This practice became a part of the typical TTP classroom in the late 1980s. A school in Japan, Tokyo Gakugei University's Setagaya Elementary School, conducted a research project to analyze students' reflective journals in the TTP classroom as a formative assessment tool (Tokyo Gakugei University Setagaya Elementary School, 1985). They coined the term *Gakushuu Kansou* to define the practice of asking students to write reflections. As Setagaya Elementary continued to research the most effective ways of using student reflections, other schools began to adopt their practices (Nakamura, 1989). The results of these studies suggest that it is best to not give students specific instructions on what to write. By letting students write freely, teachers can see what each student took away from the lesson and how they feel about what they learned. Instead of telling students what to write, it can be helpful to read selections from their reflections and give brief positive feedback. Sharing selections with the class at the beginning of the next lesson will also encourage students to write more in their own reflections. After a few weeks of implementing this technique, students will record more about other students' ideas and what happened in class that day. Contemporary mathematics textbooks in Japan include examples and encouraging prompts for inspiring meaningful reflections for each grade level (e.g., Fujii & Majima, 2020a, 2020b).

Write on the Board: Make Students' Thinking and the Discussion Visible

Neriage can be intense and often hard for some students to follow, especially in lower elementary classes. Students may struggle to put their thoughts into words and interpret their classmates' explanations. Tools, such as diagrams and mathematical expressions, can help students visualize, explain, and understand each other's approaches. Visualization is especially necessary when comparing multiple approaches. One of the reasons why Japanese mathematics classrooms use a large writing board, rather than an overhead projector or a small poster board, is to help students visualize the whole class discussion (Stevenson & Stigler, 1992; Stigler & Hiebert, 1999; Yoshida, 1999, 2005). Teachers work hard to make student thinking visible using pictures, diagrams, written words, mathematical expressions, and sometimes even cartoons, to help the class see what they are discussing.

Japanese teachers use the term *Bansho* to describe the practice of writing on the board. There are several resources in Japan on practical board writing techniques (e.g., Yanase, 1990). Some basic techniques include how to organize lesson content and how to draw diagrams so students in the back of the classroom can still see. However, effective *Bansho* requires more than just mastering basic techniques. When planning a TTP lesson, teachers need to consider what, where, and how they will write on the board. They must take into consideration the objective of the lesson, the nature of the problem, anticipated student responses, and their plan for the whole class discussion. Writing on the board serves as a clear record of the students' learning process. Since one of the goals of Level 3 teaching is to value the process of mathematics, teachers need their students to be able to look back on their ideas and how they compare to their classmates' ideas.

It is also important to develop students' note-taking skills. If students can write clear notes on their thought process, this will help them explain their ideas to others. They can use their notes to show what prior learning, diagrams, and/or operations they used to come up with their answers. Students' notes also help the teacher easily see and keep track of their progress during class time. Teachers can also collect the notebooks to read after class to gain additional insights. These notes can be an excellent data source for formative assessments. And, of course, clear notes can be a valuable resource to the students themselves, to help them recall what they have learned.

Ask Questions: Inspire Mathematical Discovery

In everyday life, when we ask a question it is generally because we don't know the answer. However, TTP teachers ask questions to help students realize how they can solve a problem. Japanese teachers call these questions *Hatsumon*. *Hatsumon* invite students to realize critical mathematical ideas and develop new mathematical procedures on their own.

Let's take the ring toss lesson as an example. The teacher never asked if the game was fair. Instead, she created a situation which prompted the students to complain. Once the students agreed that the game was not fair, the teacher wrote the following *Hatsumon* on the board, "Think about how we can all stand side by side in order to make this ring toss game fair." She stipulated that all the students have to toss their rings at the same time, so no one could suggest that they throw their rings from the same spot one after the other. The teacher crafted the question to challenge students to come up with a way that they could all stand an equal distance from the pole at the same time.

Note that the teacher did not ask, "What kind of shape can you make so everybody can stand the *same distance* from the pole?" Teachers sometimes provide more hints than necessary because they don't want to see their students struggle. However, doing so is like spoiling the end of a great detective story. Letting students enjoy tackling the challenge is the central premise of TTP. The teacher must design a thoughtful line of questioning that will inspire and not spoil the challenge. In the ring toss lesson, the teacher asks the *Hatsumon*, "Well, if this line isn't fair, what kind of line or shape do you think would make the game fair?" She doesn't use the term, "equal distance." She wants the students to realize on their own that "equal distance" is key to understanding circles. The questions a teacher asks fundamentally influence the shape of the lesson.

1.5 The Four Kinds of Whole Class Discussions (*Neriage*) in TTP

Mason, Burton, and Stacey wrote that "Mathematical thinking is provoked by contradiction, tension and surprise" (1982, p. xi). *Neriage*, the whole class discussion in a TTP lesson, strives to give students this kind of exciting and collaborative experience. The structure of *Neriage* can be flexible depending upon the topic of the lesson, the nature of the problem, and the objective of the lesson. There are four main types of *Neriage*, which I briefly introduced in section 1.4. You can introduce solutions in order of their sophistication to highlight the progression of thought, you can compare solutions to help students understand how they relate to each other, you can contrast solutions to discuss misunderstandings, and you can compare solutions to an open-ended problem to identify general rules or characteristics. In this section, I will give classroom examples that showcase each type of *Neriage* in action. In Chapter 2, I share full lesson plans that employ each type.

1.5.1 Type 1 Neriage: *Develop a New Idea by Examining the Progression of Thought*

This type of *Neriage* introduces students' various approaches in order from simplest to most sophisticated. The following vignette comes from a TTP lesson for third grade students who have already learned single-digit multiplications from 1×1 to 9×9, and division of a two-digit number divided by a single-digit number, including division with a remainder. This particular vignette was inspired by a public research lesson I observed at an elementary school affiliated with the University of Yamanashi in Yamanashi, Japan. You can view a video of the original lesson with English subtitles and read the full lesson plan on the IMPULS website (2013).

The teacher poses the following problem to the class and shows a diagram, "We are going to play one of four games, Game A, Game B, Game C, and Game D, once a week, every week, in order. What game we will play on week 26?" (Figure 1.5.01). She asks students to try to figure out the answer on their own. While they work, she walks around the classroom using a seating chart to help her jot down which students are using what strategy. After letting students work on their own for about five minutes, the teacher then opens up a whole class discussion of their work. She starts by calling on a student who counted up the weeks one by one using the diagram of the problem (Figure 1.5.01):

S: I tried to use multiplication facts of 4, but 26 isn't one of them. So I counted the weeks one by one using the diagram.
T: Okay, why don't you come to the board and count for us.
S: Week 1, week 2, week 3 . . . [The class counts along with the student] . . . week 26 is Game B.

All the students agree that they will be playing Game B on week 26. When the teacher asks how many students used this counting strategy, more than two-thirds of the class raise their hands. Then the teacher calls on a student who counted the weeks using a table (Figure 1.5.02). Although only a few students used a table to help them count, the class agrees that using a table is an excellent way to see which game will be played each week. Then she asks the class if there is maybe an even faster way to figure it out:

T: We can figure out the answer by counting the weeks one by one, but I wonder if there is a quicker and easier way.
S: I tried to use multiplication facts of 4 because they always end up as Game D. But 26 is not a multiplication fact of 4. The closest multiplication fact of 4 to 26 is 24. Since the game for week 24 will be Game D, the game for week 26 will be Game B, because its two away from Game D.
T: Can you show your thinking using math sentences?
S: 4 × 6 = 24 and 24 + 2 = 26 [the student writes the math sentences on the board].

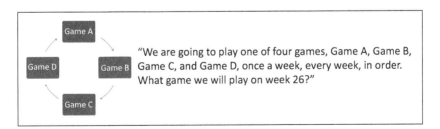

Figure 1.5.01 Type 1 *Neriage* problem example.

The teacher asks the class if they think this way of using multiplication is helpful. She also helps them examine if the idea makes sense by using the table presented earlier to help explain it. The class agrees that weeks that are multiples of 4 will all be Game D. Therefore, the 26th week, which is two weeks after the 24th week, will be Game B. The teacher makes sure that the class understands that multiplication can be used even though week 26 is not a multiplication fact of 4. The teacher then asks if anyone used any other strategies:

S: I have another way. I tried to find out how many sets of four weeks there are in 24 weeks because we will play Game D every four weeks. I used division, "26 ÷ 4 = 6 R 2." The quotient of 6 means that there are six sets of four weeks, and the remainder of 2 means that week 26 comes two weeks after we play Game D. So we will play Game B on week 26.
S: Wow, the remainder is the answer.
T: What do you mean?
S: I just realized by listening to [my classmate]'s explanation while looking at the table on the board, that all the weeks with a remainder of 2 will be Game B.
T: Are you sure? Let's see if it's true.

The class uses the table on the board (Figure 1.5.02) to examine all the weeks with a remainder of 2, e.g., week 22 (22 ÷ 4 = 5 R 2), week 18 (18 ÷ 4 = 4 R 2) ... week 6 (6 ÷ 4 = 1 R 2) to confirm that they are all Game B weeks. By discussing these four different strategies in order of their increasing complexity, all the students come to understand that they can use division to quickly and reliably solve the problem. The teacher then asks the class to apply this strategy to figure out what game they will play on other weeks, such as week 100.

The teacher anticipated that most students would solve the original problem by counting up to 26 on the diagram, and indeed that is what most students did. And if the goal of the lesson were just to find the answer, that would have been good enough. But the goal of the lesson was for students to learn something new: to appreciate that division with a remainder could be used, and that the remainder itself, rather than just representing some leftover quantity, could have an important meaning.

By starting the discussion with a method that every student understood, the teacher was able to lead students through successively more sophisticated strategies so that by the end, nearly every student had achieved the lesson goal. This type of *Neriage* allows students to begin the discussion on a level that everyone understands. The teacher's role is to carefully sequence the students' work, making sure everyone can follow along.

1.5.2   Type 2 Neriage: *Compare Multiple Approaches to Learn a New Concept*

This type of *Neriage* compares solutions side by side to uncover what they have in common. The following is an example from a fourth grade class

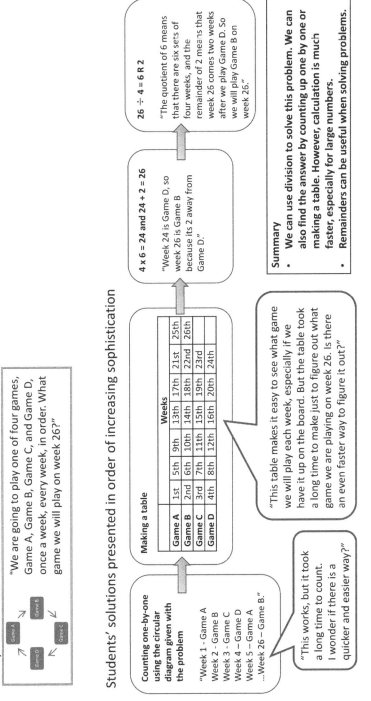

The problem

"We are going to play one of four games, Game A, Game B, Game C, and Game D, once a week, every week, in order. What game we will play on week 26?"

Students' solutions presented in order of increasing sophistication

Counting one-by-one using the circular diagram given with the problem

"Week 1 - Game A
Week 2 - Game B
Week 3 - Game C
Week 4 - Game D
Week 5 - Game A
...Week 26 - Game B".

"This works, but it took a long time to count. I wonder if there is a quicker and easier way?"

Making a table

	Weeks						
Game A	1st	5th	9th	13th	17th	21st	25th
Game B	2nd	6th	10th	14th	18th	22nd	26th
Game C	3rd	7th	11th	15th	19th	23rd	
Game D	4th	8th	12th	16th	20th	24th	

"This table makes it easy to see what game we will play each week, especially if we have it up on the board. But the table took a long time to make just to figure out what game we are playing on week 26. Is there an even faster way to figure it out?"

4 x 6 = 24 and 24 + 2 = 26

"Week 24 is Game D, so week 26 is Game B because its 2 away from Game D."

26 ÷ 4 = 6 R 2

"The quotient of 6 means that there are six sets of four weeks, and the remainder of 2 means that week 26 comes two weeks after we play Game D. So we will play Game B on week 26."

Summary
- **We can use division to solve this problem. We can also find the answer by counting up one by one or making a table. However, calculation is much faster, especially for large numbers.**
- **Remainders can be useful when solving problems.**

Figure 1.5.02 Neriage Map for the Neriage Type 1 problem example.

"There are two flowerbeds next to each other. We want to plant tulips in flowerbed A and marigolds in flowerbed B. As shown in the figure, flowerbed A is a 13 m long and 6 m wide rectangle. Flowerbed B is a 7 m long and 6 m wide rectangle. What is the total area of these two flowerbeds in m²?"

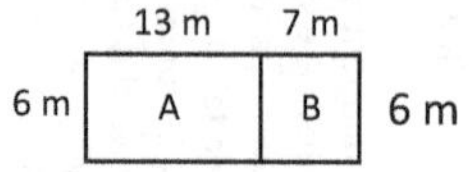

Figure 1.5.03 Type 2 *Neriage* problem example.

whose students have already studied the basic area formula for rectangles and squares. This lesson asks students to find the total area of two flowerbeds with a shared border (Figure 1.5.03) and guides them during *Neriage* so they derive the distributive property of multiplication on their own (Figure 1.5.04).

Most students will probably solve this problem by using the area formula of rectangles to find the areas of flowerbeds A and B, and then adding those two areas together (Figure 1.5.04). Another approach combines flowerbeds A and B into a single rectangle and uses the formula to find the area of that (Figure 1.5.04). By putting both solutions, $13 \times 6 + 7 \times 6 = 120$ and $(13 + 7) \times 6 = 120$, up on the board, the teacher facilitates a discussion to help students see if they both make sense. The teacher then invites the students to connect the two math sentences, $13 \times 6 + 7 \times 6 = (13 + 7) \times 6$, thus introducing the distributive property of multiplication.

1.5.3 *Type 3* **Neriage: Address Misconceptions through Debate**

Misconceptions are opportunities to help students look back and solidify their understanding of concepts. Type 3 *Neriage* utilizes a task designed to provoke both correct and incorrect solutions. The tension from the resulting contradictions is used to inspire higher level mathematical thinking (Mason et al., 1982). In the following example, students compare two shapes, a rectangle and a square, to see which one has more space inside (Figure 1.5.05). I introduced this lesson briefly as the flower bed problem in section 1.3.2. It introduces the concept of area and area measurement. Students must devise their own methods for comparing the sizes of the two shapes as they do not yet know the area formula.

There are three main approaches that students typically take to solve this problem (Figure 1.5.05). If you hand out papers of the shapes, students may cut them out and overlap them to see which one is bigger. This can help them make a visual estimate, but it's still hard to say for sure which is bigger. Students may also measure the perimeters of both shapes and come to the incorrect conclusion that because the length of the perimeters are the same, the

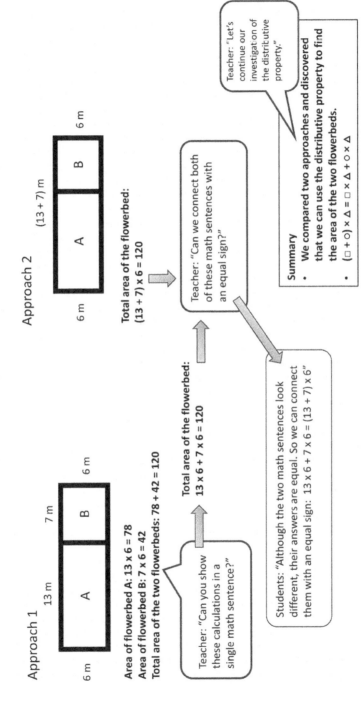

Figure 1.5.04 *Neriage* Map for the *Neriage* Type 2 problem example.

Contrast approaches to highlight a typical misunderstanding

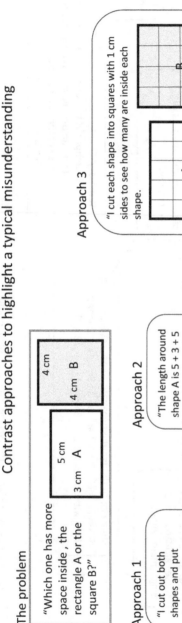

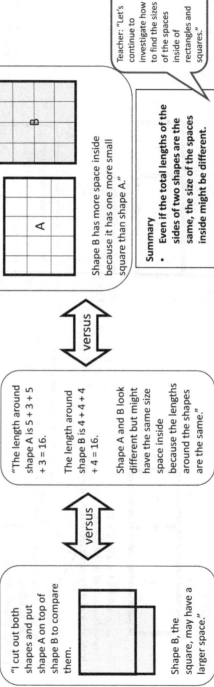

Figure 1.5.05 Neriage Map for the Neriage Type 3 problem example.

areas are also the same. Another approach that students may take is dividing up each shape into squares with 1 cm sides and counting how many of those squares are inside each shape. The shape that is made up of more squares with 1 cm sides has the larger area.

Hatsumon for this lesson would avoid asking students to find the area and perimeter of the shapes. Instead, students would be challenged to quantify the two shapes' spaces to compare them. By constructing a debate over their different solution tactics, both correct and incorrect, you can engage the class in an authentic discussion of what types of measurement can be used and how.

1.5.4 Type 4 Neriage: Compare Various Solutions to an Open-Ended Problem

The especially fluid and dynamic Type 4 *Neriage* compares students' various solutions to open-ended problems for which there are multiple correct solutions. The following example involves a hands-on investigation in which students make a variety of triangles (Figure 1.5.06). It is for students who have already been introduced to triangles and are ready to deepen their understanding.

Each student will make several triangles by selecting three straws for each triangle. There are four different lengths of straws to choose from: 12 cm, 10 cm, 8 cm, and 6 cm. They can make triangles whose lengths are all different sizes, triangles which have two sides that are equal lengths, and triangles whose sides are all the same length. If a student chooses a 10 cm straw, a 8 cm straw, and a 6 cm straw, their triangle will have a right angle. If a student chooses two 6 cm straws and one 12 cm straws, the resulting figure will not even be a triangle (in which case they can try again and later share their experience during *Neriage*). The teacher asks students to affix their triangles to paper plates so it will be easy to rotate the triangles to compare them in various orientations. Each student is encouraged to make several different triangles by repeating the above process.

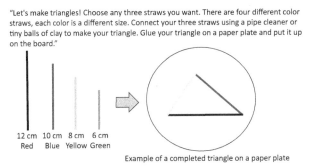

"Let's make triangles! Choose any three straws you want. There are four different color straws, each color is a different size. Connect your three straws using a pipe cleaner or tiny balls of clay to make your triangle. Glue your triangle on a paper plate and put it up on the board."

12 cm   10 cm   8 cm   6 cm
Red   Blue   Yellow Green

Example of a completed triangle on a paper plate

Figure 1.5.06 Type 4 *Neriage* problem example.

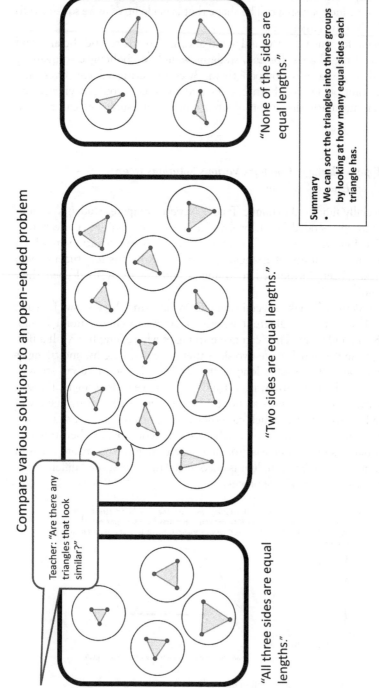

Figure 1.5.07 Neriage Map for the Neriage Type 4 problem example.

Once the class has made the full range of possible triangles and posted them up on the board, the teacher begins *Neriage* by asking if they can find any triangles that are the same. Students need to examine each triangle carefully by rotating and flipping them. The class then removes all the duplicate triangles. The teacher then asks if there are any triangles that look similar (Figure 1.5.07). Students can easily see that triangles made with three equal length straws look similar but are different sizes. The teacher asks the students to make a group with these triangles and move them all to one side of the board. The teacher then asks if there are any other triangles that have something in common. The teacher guides the students to sort all the triangles into three groups: triangles whose sides are all equal lengths, triangles with two sides that are equal lengths, and triangles whose sides are all different lengths (Figure 1.5.07). If it's appropriate for your classroom you can introduce the terms "equilateral," "isosceles," and "scalene" when summarizing the lesson after the discussion. However, the most critical idea students need to grasp is the importance of paying attention to features such as the number of sides and how those sides relate to each other. This practice lets us sort polygons into triangles, quadrilaterals, and so on. By paying attention to the lengths of the sides, you can sort out triangles into the above three groups.

1.6 Types of TTP Lessons

As I discussed in section 1.3, Japanese teachers began exploring using TTP lessons as bonus end-of-chapter activities or one-off replacements for textbook lessons. It wasn't until after years of teachers' and researchers' experiments that TTP lessons became an integral part of the curriculum. I have organized contemporary TTP lessons into three categories: lessons to develop conceptual and procedural understanding, lessons to expand understanding, and lessons with multiple correct solutions. I will introduce all three types below. I also present several full lesson plans for each type in Chapter 2 so you can try them in your classroom.

1.6.1 TTP Lessons to Develop Conceptual and Procedural Understanding

TTP lessons in this category are presented in a series as textbook units or modules. A rising number of Japanese mathematics textbooks have recently begun to incorporate this practice (e.g., Fujii & Majima, 2020b). A unit opens with a TTP lesson to introduce a new concept, and expands upon that concept through a series of TTP lessons. Each lesson is carefully designed to build upon the previous lesson.

These units or modules generally begin by letting students explore a new mathematical concept by attacking an unfamiliar problem. They must then apply what they learned from this opening problem to similar situations or related exercises to solidify their understanding. They are then given new situations to expand upon what they have learned so far in the unit or module. Each new situation may be followed up by related practice exercises; these lessons can span several days depending on the topic and objective. At the end of the unit/module, students look back on what they learned and become fluent utilizing the knowledge, procedures, and practices they discovered.

In Chapter 2, I include five units that exemplify this type of TTP lesson, "Using an equation to express a situation: A series of matchstick problems," "Can you add these numbers without counting one by one?," "Ideas for quantifying crowdedness and speed," "Deriving the area formula of a parallelogram," and "Introducing fractions." Each unit is made up of several lessons that guide students to develop conceptual and procedural understanding of each unit topic.

1.6.2 TTP Lessons to Expand Understanding

TTP lessons in this category are typically found at the end of a unit or a module to expand upon what students have been studying. This kind of lesson requires students to use their problem-solving skills and mathematical thinking to apply their knowledge to a new situation. These challenging TTP lessons help students make new connections among what they have already learned in previous units. One of the advantages of this kind of TTP lesson is that students can grapple with the problem at various entry points, therefore classrooms whose students display a wide range of abilities can all jump right in. For the same reason, this kind of TTP lesson also readily engages the whole class in fruitful discussion.

In Chapter 2, I include five lessons that exemplify this type of TTP lesson, "Curious subtraction," "Comparing areas using pattern blocks," "Let's make a calendar," "Finding the area of triangles inside parallelograms," and "Devising ways to construct a congruent triangle."

1.6.3 TTP Lessons with Multiple Correct Solutions

This category of TTP lesson utilizes an open-ended problem to allow students to explore new ideas and mathematical insights. This type of TTP lesson can be used in a variety of ways throughout the curriculum. It can introduce a unit, act as a replacement for certain pages in a unit, or be a fun in-between unit activity. Research has shown that open-ended problems provide an ideal opportunity to assess students' abilities (Becker & Shimada, 1997; Shimada, 1977). Furthermore, because an open-ended problem will generate a wide variety of student solutions, they inspire particularly dynamic whole class discussions.

In Chapter 2, I include four lessons that exemplify this type of TTP lesson, "Opening a cube," "How many different squares can you make on a geoboard?," "Find all the isosceles triangles on a geoboard," and "Let's create new math problems! A lesson from the book *Mondai kara Mondai e [From Problem to Problem]*."

References

Ball, D. L., Thames, M. H., & Phelps, G. (2008). Content Knowledge for Teaching: What Makes It Special? *Journal of Teacher Education, 59*(5), 389–407. doi:10.11 77/0022487108324554

Banilower, E. R., Smith, P. S., Malzahn, K. A., Plumley, C. L., Gordon, E. M., & Hayes, M. L. (2018). *Report of the 2018 NSSME+*. Retrieved from https://eric.ed. gov/?id=ED541798

Bass, H., Usiskin, Z. P., & Burrill, G. (Eds.). (2002). *Studying Classroom Teaching as a Medium for Professional Development. Proceedings of a U.S.–Japan Workshop (July 31– August 6, 2000)*. Washington, DC: National Academy Press.

Becker, J. P., & Miwa, T. (1987). *Proceedings of the U.S.–Japan Seminar on Mathematical Problem-solving (Honolulu, Hawaii, July 14–18, 1986)* (INT-8514988). Carbondale, IL: Southern Illinois University. Retrieved from www.academia.edu/21652649/Pro ceedings_of_the_U_S_Japan_Seminar_on_Mathematical_Problem_Solving_Hon olulu_Hawaii_July_14_18_1986_

Becker, J. P., & Shimada, S. (1997). *The Open-ended Approach: A New Proposal for Teaching mathematics*. Reston, VA: National Council of Teachers of Mathematics.

Becker, J. P., Silver, E. A., Kantowski, M. G., Travers, K. J., & Wilson, J. W. (1990). Some Observations of Mathematics Teaching in Japanese Elementary and Junior High Schools. *Arithmetic Teacher, 38*(2), 12–21.

Charles, R., & Lester, F. (1983). *Teaching Problem-solving: What, Why and How* (K. Nakashima, Trans.). Japan: Kaneko Shobou.

Common Core State Standards Initiative. (2010). Common Core State Standards for Mathematics. Retrieved from www.corestandards.org/Math/

Fujii, T. (2016). Designing and Adapting Tasks in Lesson Planning: A Critical Process of Lesson Study. *ZDM*, 1–13.

Fujii, T., & Majima, H. (2020a). *Atarashii Sansuu [New Mathematics]*. Tokyo: Tokyo Shoseki.

Fujii, T., & Majima, H. (2020b). *New Mathematics for Elementary School* (A. Takahashi & T. Watanabe, Trans.). Tokyo: Tokyo Shoseki.

Gattegno, C. (1970). Notes on a New Epistemology: Teaching and Education. *Math Teaching, 50*, 2–5.

IMPULS. (2013). Division with Remainders: Utilizing Remainders. Retrieved from www.impuls-tgu.org/en/library/number_and_operation/page-116.html

International Bureau of Education. (1995). Glossary of Curriculum Terminology. Retrieved from http://dmz-ibe2.vm.unesco.org/en/glossary-curriculum-terminology

Iyanaga, S. (1954). *Atarashii Sansuu [New Mathematics]*. Tokyo: Tokyo Shoseki.

Iyanaga, S. (1976). *Atarashii Sansuu [New Mathematics]*. Tokyo: Tokyo Shoseki.

Lesh, R., & Zawojewski, J. (2007). Problem-solving and Modeling. In F. K. Lester Jr (Ed.), *Second Handbook of Research on Mathematics Teaching and Learning: A Project of the National Council of Teachers of Mathematics*. Charlotte, North Carolina: Informa tion Age Publishing.

Lewis, C., & Tsuchida, I. (1998). A Lesson is Like a Swiftly Flowing River. *American Educator* (Winter 1998), 12–51.

Ma, L. (1999). *Knowing and Teaching Elementary Mathematics: Teachers' Understanding of Fundamental Mathematics in China and the United States*: Hillsdale, NJ: Lawrence Erlbaum Associates.

Maehara, S., & Sugiyama, Y. (1992). *Atarashii Sansuu [New Mathematics]*. Tokyo: Tokyo Shoseki.

Makinae, N. (2019). The Origin and Development of Lesson Study in Japan. In R. Huang, A. Takahashi, & J. da Ponte (Eds.), *Theory and Practice of Lesson Study in Mathematics* (pp. 170–181). New York: Springer International Publishing.

Mason, J., Burton, L., & Stacey, K. (1982). *Thinking Mathematically*. London: Addison-Wesley Publishing.

Michigan State University. (1996). *The Connected Mathematics (CMP)*. Ann Arbor, MI: Michigan State University.

Ministry of Education Japan. (1958). National Curriculum Standards (1958 Revision). Retrieved from www.nier.go.jp/guideline/s33e/index.htm

Ministry of Education Japan. (1989a). *Elementary School Teaching Guide: Arithmetic*. Tokyo: Toyokan Publishing.

Ministry of Education Japan. (1989b). *National Curriculum Standards (1989 Revision)*. Tokyo: Okurasho Publishing Bureau. Retrieved from www.nier.go.jp/guideline/h01e/index.htm

Mullis, I. V. S. (2000). TIMSS 1999 International Mathematics Report: Findings from the IEA's Repeat of the Third International Mathematics and Science Study at the Eighth Grade. Retrieved from http://timss.bc.edu/timss1999i/math_achievement_report.html

Mullis, I. V. S., Martin, M. O., & Loveless, T. (2016). *20 Years of TIMSS: International Trends in Mathematics and Science Achievement, Curriculum, and Instruction*. Boston, MA: TIMSS & PIRLS International Study Center, Lynch School of Education, Boston College.

Nakamura, T. (1989). How Learning Impression Should Be in Order to Cultivate the Mathematical Reasoning: Teaching Areas to Fourth Graders. *Journal of Japan Society of Mathematical Education. Mathematical Education*, 71(2), 14–21. Retrieved from https://ci.nii.ac.jp/naid/110003731738/en/

Nakashima, K. (1997). *Mathematics Education, 50 Years: The Trajectory of Progress*. Tokyo: Toyokan Publishing.

National Council of Teachers of Mathematics. (1980). *An Agenda for Action: Recommendations for School Mathematics of the 1980s*. Reston, VA: National Council of Teachers of Mathematics.

National Council of Teachers of Mathematics. (1989). *Curriculum and Evaluation Standards for School Mathematics*. Reston, VA: National Council of Teachers of Mathematics.

National Council of Teachers of Mathematics. (2000). *Principles and Standards for School Mathematics*. Reston, VA: National Council of Teachers of Mathematics.

National Research Council. (2001). *Adding it Up: Helping Children Learn Mathematics*. Washington, DC: National Academy Press.

Polya, G. (1945). *How to Solve it: A New Aspect of Mathematical Method*. Princeton, NJ: Princeton University Press.

Polya, G. (1954). *How to Solve it: A New Aspect of Mathematical Method* (Y. Kakiuti, Trans.). Japan: Maruzen.

Sansuu Jyugyou Kenkyuukai. (1994). *Rethinking Mathematics Problem Solving Lessons*. Tokyo: Toyokan Publishing.

Schmidt, W. H., McKnight, C. C., Valverde, G., Houang, R. T., & Wiley, D. E. (1997). *Many Visions, Many Aims: A Cross-National Investigation of Curricular Intentions in School Mathematics*. Dordrecht: Springer Netherlands.

Schoenfeld, A. H. (1985). *Mathematical problem-solving*. Orlando, FL: Academic Press.

Schroeder, T. L., & Lester, F. (1989). Developing Understanding in Mathematics via Problem-solving. In P. R. Trafton (Ed.), *New directions for elementary school mathematics* (pp. 31–42). Reston, VA: NCTM.

Shimada, S. (1977). *Open Ended Approach in Mathematics*. Tokyo: Mizuumi Shobo.

Shimizu, Y. (1999). Aspects of Mathematics Teacher Education in Japan: Focusing on Teachers' Role. *Journal of Mathematics Teacher Education*, 2(1), 107–116.

Shimizu, Y. (2003). Problem-solving as a Vehicle for Teaching Mathematics: A Japanese Perspective. In F. K. Lester (Ed.), *Teaching Mathematics through Problem-solving: Grades Pre K–6* (pp. 205–214). Reston, VA: National Council of Teachers of Mathematics.

Stevenson, H. (1980). The Polished Stones. Retrieved from www.youtube.com/watch?v=Tpr6Q2FsJyE

Stevenson, H., & Stigler, J. (1992). *The Learning Gap*. New York: Summit.

Stigler, J., & Hiebert, J. (1999). *The Teaching Gap: Best Ideas from the World's Teachers for Improving Education in the Classroom*. New York: Free Press.

Stigler, J., & Hiebert, J. (2009). Closing the Teaching Gap. *Phi Delta Kappan*, 91(03), 32–37.

Sugiyama, Y. (2008). *Introduction to Elementary Mathematics Education*. Tokyo: Toyokan Publishing Co.

Takahashi, A. (1996). Open-ended Problem-solving in Japanese Elementary Schools. Paper presented at the International Congress on Mathematical Education 8, Sevilla, Spain.

Takahashi, A. (2008). Beyond Show and Tell: Neriage for Teaching Through Problem-solving – Ideas from Japanese Problem-solving Approaches for Teaching Mathematics. Paper presented at the 11th International Congress on Mathematics Education in Mexico (Section TSG 19: Research and Development in Problem-solving in Mathematics Education), Monterrey, Mexico.

Takahashi, A. (2011). The Japanese Approach to Developing Expertise in Using the Textbook to Teach Mathematics rather than Teaching the Textbook. In Y. Li & G. Kaiser (Eds.), *Expertise in Mathematics Instruction: An International Perspective* (pp. 197–219). New York: Springer.

Takeuchi, Y., & Sawada, T. (1984). *Mondai kara Mondai e [From Problem to Problem]*. Tokyo: Toyokan Publishing.

Tokyo Gakugei University Setagaya Elementary School. (1985). *Jyugyou wo tsukuru [Designing lessons]*. Tokyo: Toyokan.

Travers, K. J. (2011). The Second International Mathematics Study (SIMS): Intention, Implementation, Attainment. In C. Papanastasiou, T. Plomp, & E. C. Papanastasiou (Eds.), *IEA 1958–2008: 50 Years of Experiences and Memories* (pp. 73–96). Amsterdam: The International Association for the Evaluation of Educational Achievement (IEA).

Travers, K. J., & Westbury, I. (1989). The IEA Study of Mathematics I: Analysis of Mathematics Curricula. Supplement. Retrieved from https://eric.ed.gov/?id=ED306111

University of Chicago School Mathematics Project. (1992). *Everyday Mathematics*. Chicago, IL: University of Chicago.

Watanabe, T. (2014). Transformation of Japanese Elementary Mathematics Textbooks: 1958–2012. In Y. Li, E. Silver, & S. Li (Eds.), *Transforming Mathematics Instruction: Multiple Approaches and Practices* (pp. 199–216). Heidelberg: Springer.

Wei, R. C., Darling-Hammond, L., Andree, A., Richardson, N., & Orphanos, S. (2009). *Professional Learning in the Learning Profession: A Status Report on Teacher Development in the U.S. and Abroad.* Technical Report. Dallas, TX: National Staff Development Council.

Yanase, O. (1990). *Sansuu-Tanoshii Bansho no Gihou [Techniques for Enjoyable Board Writing in Mathematics].* Tokyo: Nihon Shoseki.

Yoshida, M. (1999). Lesson Study: A Case Study of a Japanese Approach to Improving Instruction through School-based Teacher Development. Dissertation, University of Chicago, Chicago, IL.

Yoshida, M. (2005). Using Lesson Study to Develop Effective Blackboard Practice. In P. Wang-Iverson & M. Yoshida (Eds.), *Building Our Understanding of Lesson Study* (pp. 93–100). Philadelphia, PA: Research for Better Schools.

2 TTP Lessons You Can Use

The Japanese approach of TTP uses problem-solving as an integral part of every lesson for every grade. TTP can be used to introduce new knowledge, procedures, and strategies. It can expand students' understanding by giving them new situations in which to apply their knowledge. It can also reinforce how to think mathematically through open-ended problems with multiple correct solutions. This chapter opens with five units of problem-solving lessons that develop conceptual and procedural understanding to show how you can use problem-solving to teach new material in your daily lessons. It also includes five spotlight lessons which require students to extend their understanding of mathematics, and four spotlight lessons which feature open-ended problems that facilitate students' ability to think mathematically. These examples are based on ideas from Japanese classrooms but are specifically selected to address CCSS-M topics (Common Core State Standards Initiative, 2010). The TTP lessons collected in this chapter range from lower elementary to lower secondary grade levels.

Since the effectiveness of the TTP lessons depends on the students' prior learning, the teachers may need to fine-tune the following examples to fit into your student needs. Thus, I strongly recommend you adjust these lessons to suit your classroom based on the advice outlined in section 1.4.3.

2.1 TTP Lessons to Develop Conceptual and Procedural Understanding

The TTP lessons in this section form a unit to address specific standards through a series of TTP lessons. Each lesson is designed to build onto the previous lesson to help students achieve the objective(s) of the unit. It may not be a good idea to skip or reorder any of these lessons unless you think doing so is necessary to engage your students based on formative assessment.

2.1.1 TTP Unit: "Building a Bridge from Arithmetic to Algebra"

Grade: Upper elementary

In this unit, students will use mathematical expressions to represent various ways of counting, understand what each number in the mathematical expression represents, and use those mathematical expressions to solve problems.

PRIOR LEARNING REQUIRED

- CCSS.Math.Content.3.OA "Solve problems involving the four operations, and identify and explain patterns in arithmetic."
- CCSS.Math.Content.4.OA "Use the four operations with whole numbers to solve problems."
- CCSS.Math.Content.5.OA.A.1 "Use parentheses, brackets, or braces in numerical expressions, and evaluate expressions with these symbols."

MAIN CCSS ADDRESSED IN THIS UNIT

- CCSS.Math.Content.4.OA.C.5 "Generate a number or shape pattern that follows a given rule. Identify apparent features of the pattern that were not explicit in the rule itself."
- CCSS.Math.Content.5.OA.A.2 "Write simple expressions that record calculations with numbers, and interpret numerical expressions without evaluating them."

RELATED LATER LEARNING

- CCSS.Math.Content.6.EE.A.2.A "Write expressions that record operations with numbers and with letters standing for numbers."
- CCSS.Math.Content.6.EE.B.6 "Use variables to represent numbers and write expressions when solving a real-world or mathematical problem; understand that a variable can represent an unknown number, or, depending on the purpose at hand, any number in a specified set."
- CCSS.Math.Content.6.EE.C "Represent and analyze quantitative relationships between dependent and independent variables."

This unit is designed to teach the usefulness of mathematical expressions. Each lesson in this unit is based on problems typically used in Japanese classrooms, and some of them are used in Japanese textbooks, such as *Mathematics International* (Fujii & Iitaka, 2012). Students will learn the value of mathematical expressions as they solve a series of problems on their own and compare their solutions with various approaches made by their peers. This unit builds on the students' prior learning. They have been using mathematical expressions since kindergarten to express quantitative relationships in story problems with everyday contexts. This creates the foundation for understanding the usefulness of mathematical expressions to determine what operations can be used to solve a problem.

This unit also establishes the crucial foundation for learning algebra. It helps students see the value of mathematical expressions and develops their ability to make generalizations about a given mathematical situation. In this unit, students learn how they can use mathematical expressions to represent different ways of counting. They will experience the contrast between the convenience of using mathematical expressions and the difficulty of laboriously counting each object one by one. Students will also recognize that as the number of objects they are counting changes, some of the numbers in their mathematical expressions change, while other numbers in the expression stay the same. This reflects "quasi-variable" understanding, defined by Fujii and Stephens as the ability to make arithmetic generalizations about the relationships between numbers in a given mathematical situation (Fujii & Stephens, 2001). In algebra, students use equations with letters to represent two quantities that change in relationship to one another. The quasi-variable understanding taught in this unit is essential to prepare upper elementary students for the algebra units they will encounter later.

Students will also develop necessary skills as dictated by the Common Core State Standards for Mathematical Practice SMP (2010) in this unit. They will not only communicate their own reasoning to others by expressing their own ways of counting using mathematical expressions, but also infer their peers' ways of thinking by interpreting each other's mathematical expressions. They will have to justify the reasonableness of their own and each other's counting strategies and mathematical expressions. This experience is expected to foster their skills for developing viable arguments and critiquing each other's reasoning, which directly relates to SMP3 (Common Core State Standards Initiative, 2010). Furthermore, the process of writing and interpreting mathematical expressions will also help students develop the ability to reason quantitatively and abstractly, which relates to SMP2 (Common Core State Standards Initiative, 2010).

By recognizing the generalizability of the mathematical expressions they write to express their ways of counting, students will see the value of mathematical expressions for determining the number of objects when counting one by one is too difficult. This should help them realize the usefulness of using mathematical expressions as a model for expressing mathematical situations, which relates to SMP4 (Common Core State Standards Initiative, 2010). It is also expected that the students will grow in their ability to use mathematical expressions to analyze relationships mathematically and draw conclusions, which also relates to SMP4 (Common Core State Standards Initiative, 2010). This will create the foundation for them to represent two quantities that change in relationship to one another by using variables.

In the first lesson of the unit, students will explore a task by using a variety of ways of counting. They will discuss how to count the number of dots in the diagram (Figure 2.1.1.01). They will first work independently to come up with creative ways of counting the total number of dots. Then, each student will represent their ways of counting in a mathematical expression. Through a whole class discussion, the students will share their mathematical expressions with the class, and infer each other's methods of counting by interpreting these mathematical expressions. After the discussion, the class will summarize all the creative ways of counting the dots.

In the second lesson, two diagrams (Figures 2.1.1.02 and 2.1.1.03) will be given and students will use what they learned from the first lesson

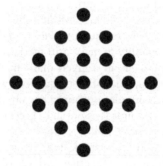

Figure 2.1.1.01

Figure 2.1.1.02

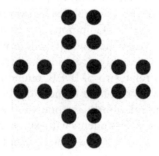

Figure 2.1.1.03

to discuss effective ways to organize the dots into equal groups. They will again be asked to think about how to count the number of dots, write their ideas as mathematical expressions, and to compare and discuss those ideas as a class. This question is designed for students to explore the generalizability of mathematical expressions. The dots in the diagrams from lessons 1 and 2 can be counted one by one, which makes it easy to verify the results obtained from mathematical expressions.

In the third lesson, students use what they learned from lessons 1 and 2 to find the number of dots without counting one by one. Students will be asked to find the total number of dots in a diagram (Figure 2.1.1.04). To expand on their learning, students will also be asked to find the total number of the dots when each side of the diagram becomes 10 dots. Although they will be encouraged to find out the total number without drawing the diagram, any student who needs to may do so. This task provides a transition for students to see the possibility of using mathematical expressions to find the total number of dots in the absence of an actual diagram. During the classroom discussion, the teacher will ask students to compare the mathematical expressions they created for the original diagram with the expressions they created when there are 10 dots on each side. The teacher will ask which numbers in their mathematical expressions change and which stay the same. This discussion of quasi-variable understanding helps students recognize on their own that their mathematical expressions may be generalized, and prepares them for the concept of variables that they will encounter later when they learn algebra.

Figure 2.1.1.04

Figure 2.1.1.05

The fourth lesson applies all the learning from the previous three lessons to a different situation. The stick problem (Figure 2.1.1.05) will be presented. Students will be asked to determine the number of sticks required to make a row of 30 adjacent squares. Counting one by one is not an option because the number of sticks involved would be too large. Instead, they must utilize what they experienced in previous lessons about the generalizability of mathematical expressions to come up with mathematical expressions to find the total number of sticks needed. In the whole class discussion, students will examine their various mathematical expressions to see if they are reasonable. The fifth lesson is a chance for students to review the learning of the unit and practice their newfound skills with additional interesting problems.

Each of these problem-solving lessons will foster students' reasoning by challenging them to come up with ways to find the number of objects in a pattern, to represent their ways of thinking in mathematical expressions, and to justify whether a mathematical expression is reasonable and correct. Students will also have opportunities to discuss the rules of arithmetic calculation, such as the use of parentheses and the order of operations.

UNIT FLOW

Lesson	Lesson title and main learning objectives	Time
1	"Let's think about ways to count the number of dots"	60 min
	Students will try to represent their ways of counting dots in mathematical expressions and infer other students' ways of counting from their mathematical expressions.	
2	"Use mathematical expressions to show your ways of counting"	60 min
	Students will be able to represent their ways of counting dots using mathematical expressions and will infer other students' ways of counting from their mathematical expressions. Students will explore the generalizability of mathematical expressions with a simple diagram that is easy to verify by counting.	
3	"Find the number of dots without counting one by one"	60 min
	Students will use mathematical expressions to represent the number of dots and find the total number of dots in a larger version of the diagram without counting one by one. Students are encouraged to use mathematical expressions instead of drawing and counting, but those who need to may do so.	
4	"How many sticks are there altogether?"	60 min
	Students will represent their ways of counting sticks in mathematical expressions and use their mathematical expressions to determine the number of sticks. The numbers are too large to draw and count, so students must apply what they've learned about the generalizability of mathematical expressions.	
5	"Summarize and additional exercises"	60 min

Lesson 1: "Let's Think about Ways to Count the Number of Dots"

OBJECTIVES

- Students will represent their ways of counting dots in mathematical expressions and infer other students' ways of counting from their mathematical expressions.
- Students will examine mathematical expressions using their prior learning of the order of operations and use of parentheses.

LESSON FLOW

Steps, questions from the teacher, activities, and anticipated student responses	Support from the teacher	Check understanding
 **1. Introduction** Understand how to represent ways of counting in mathematical expressions in simple cases. Use the two diagrams (Figure 2.1.1.06) to help students see how mathematical expressions can be used to show ways of counting the number of dots.	Briefly show the diagrams one at a time. Encourage students to share their ways of counting the number of dots in the diagrams. Remind students that multiplication is *(number in each group)* × *(number of groups)*	Do students understand what it means to show their way of counting by using a mathematical expression?

$4 + 1 = 5$ $2 \times 4 = 8$ $4 \times 2 = 8$

Figure 2.1.1.06

Help students remember that 2×4 and 4×2 are different ways of looking at the same diagram

2. Posing the problem Show the diagram (Figure 2.1.1.07) and ask the following question:	If any students seem to not understand the task, share a few of the other students' work as examples. 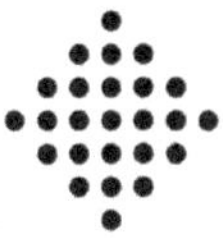	Do students understand that the task is to represent ways of counting using mathematical expressions?

"Think about ways to count the number of dots in the picture. Write a math sentence (mathematical expression) that describes your method for each way of counting."

Figure 2.1.1.07

Steps, questions from the teacher, activities, and anticipated student responses	*Support from the teacher*	*Check understanding*
3. Student problem-solving/ anticipated student responses 1. Decomposing 25 in arbitrary ways. E.g., *10 + 10 + 5 = 25, 12 x 2 + 1 = 25* 2. Making groups of dots in the diagram. E.g., *1 + 3 + 5 + 7 + 5 + 3 + 1 = 25*, or, *(1 + 3 + 5) x 2 + 7 = 25* 3. Making equal groups and using multiplication. E.g., *3 x 8 + 1 = 25* *5 x 5 = 25* *3 x 3 + 4 x 4 = 25*	Let each student write their ways of counting and corresponding mathematical expressions in their notes. Use a seating chart to note each student's way of counting and mathematical expressions to prepare for the whole class discussion.	Does each student come up with at least one mathematical expression to represent how to count the number of dots?

Figure 2.1.1.08

4. Comparison and discussion For each mathematical expression: 1. Ask one of the students who came up with a mathematical expression to show it to the class. 2. Let the other students infer how they counted the dots by interpreting the mathematical expression. 3. Let the student who came up with the mathematical expression explain why that inference is correct or not. Repeat the above until students understand the variety of ways to count the number of dots by making equal groups.	Let students infer each other's ways of counting to help them see that a mathematical expression can communicate a way of thinking. Help them recall their prior learning, such as the meanings of operations and the order of operations. See if they can represent their ways of counting correctly.	Do students use operations and the order of operations correctly? Do students understand that they can infer a way of counting from an expression?
5. Summarizing Help each student identify the learning from the class and record it in their notes. • Mathematical expressions can be used to show ways of counting the number of dots. • Making equal groups will help you use multiplication to find the total number of dots easily.		Does each student summarize their learning and record it in their notes?

Lesson 2: "Use Mathematical Expressions to Show Your Ways of Counting"

OBJECTIVES

- Students will use the learning from Lesson 1 to become comfortable representing their ways of counting dots in mathematical expressions and inferring other students' ways of counting from their mathematical expressions.
- Students will use their prior learning of the order of operations and use of parentheses to represent and interpret mathematical expressions correctly.

LESSON FLOW

Steps, questions from the teacher, activities, and anticipated student responses	Support from the teacher	Check understanding
1. Introduction Let a few students read their journal reflections from Lesson 1 and help the class recall what they learned. Give students a warm-up problem. Show the diagram and ask the following question: 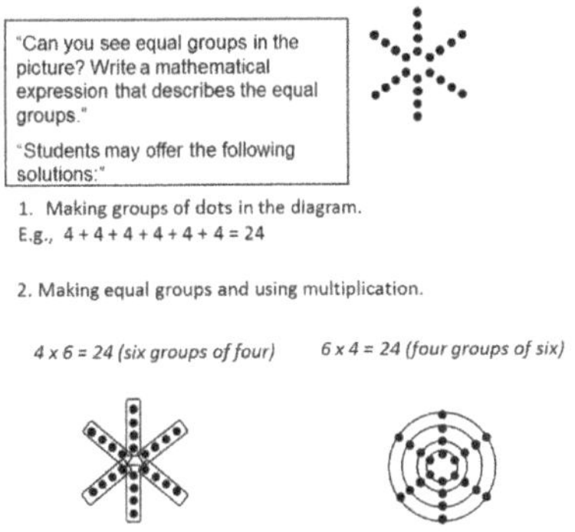	Before the class, select a few exemplary journal reflections from Lesson 1.	Are students ready for the new problem?

"Can you see equal groups in the picture? Write a mathematical expression that describes the equal groups."
"Students may offer the following solutions:"

1. Making groups of dots in the diagram.
E.g., 4 + 4 + 4 + 4 + 4 + 4 = 24

2. Making equal groups and using multiplication.

$4 \times 6 = 24$ *(six groups of four)* $6 \times 4 = 24$ *(four groups of six)*

Figure 2.1.1.09

2. Posing the problem Show the diagram and ask the following question: 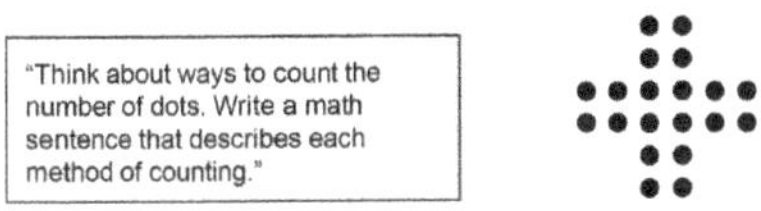	If any students seem to not understand the task, share a few of the other students' work as examples.	Do students understand that the task is to represent ways of counting with mathematical expressions?

"Think about ways to count the number of dots. Write a math sentence that describes each method of counting."

Figure 2.1.1.10

(Continued)

Steps, questions from the teacher, activities, and anticipated student responses	Support from the teacher	Check understanding
3. Student problem-solving / anticipated student responses	Let each student write their ways of counting and mathematical expressions in their notes.	Does each student come up with at least one mathematical expression to represent how to count the number of dots?

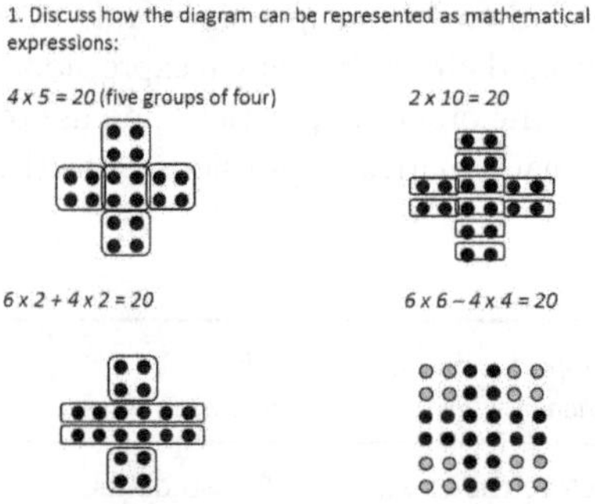

1. Discuss how the diagram can be represented as mathematical expressions:

4 x 5 = 20 (five groups of four)   2 x 10 = 20

6 x 2 + 4 x 2 = 20   6 x 6 − 4 x 4 = 20

Use a seating chart to note each student's way of counting and mathematical expressions to prepare for the whole class discussion.

Figure 2.1.1.11

4. Comparison and discussion	Help students infer each other's ways of counting and help them see that a mathematical expression can communicate a way of thinking.	Do students use operations and the order of operations correctly?

For each mathematical expression:

1. Ask one of the students who came up with a mathematical expression to show it to the class.
2. Let the other students infer how they counted the dots by interpreting the mathematical expression.
3. Let the student who came up with the mathematical expression explain why that inference is correct or not.

Repeat the above until students understand a variety of ways to count the number of dots by making equal groups.

Help them recall their prior learning, such as the meanings of operations and the order of operations to see if they can represent their ways of counting correctly.

5. Summarizing

Help each student identify the learning from the class and record it in their notes.

- Mathematical expressions can be used to show ways of counting the number of dots.
- Making equal groups helps you use multiplication to find the total number of dots easily.

Does each student summarize their learning and record it in their notes?

Lesson 3: "Find the Number of Dots Without Counting One By One"

OBJECTIVES

- Students will represent their ways of counting dots in mathematical expressions and infer other students' ways of counting from their mathematical expressions.
- Students will use the mathematical expressions they develop while counting the dots when there are 7 dots on each side of the square to determine the total number of dots when the number of dots on each side is changed.

LESSON FLOW

Steps, questions from the teacher, activities, and anticipated student responses	Support from the teacher	Check understanding
1. Introduction Let a few students read their journal reflections from Lesson 2 and help the class to recall what they learned.	Before the class, select a few exemplary journal reflections from Lesson 2.	Are students ready for the new problem?
2. Posing the problem Show the diagram and ask the following question: "Think about ways to count the number of dots in the picture shown. Write a math sentence for each of your methods." *Figure 2.1.1.12*	Help students see that there are 7 dots on each side of the square.	Do students understand that the task is to represent ways of counting using mathematical expressions? Do they understand 4 × 7 is not correct?
3. Student problem-solving/anticipated student responses 1) Making groups of dots in the diagram. 7 x 2 + 5 x 2 = 24 7 x 4 - 4 = 24 5 x 4 + 4 = 24 6 x 4 = 24 3 x 8 = 24 7 x 7 − 5 x 5 = 24 *Figure 2.1.1.13*	Let each student write their ways of counting and mathematical expressions in their notes. Use a seating chart to note each student's way of counting and mathematical expressions to prepare for the whole class discussion.	Does each student come up with at least one mathematical expression to represent how to count the number of dots?

Steps, questions from the teacher, activities, and anticipated student responses	Support from the teacher	Check understanding
4. Comparison and discussion For each mathematical expression: 1. Ask one of the students who came up with a mathematical expression to show it to the class. 2. Let the other students infer how they counted the dots by interpreting the mathematical expression. 3. Let the student who came up with the mathematical expression explain why that inference is correct or not. Repeat the above until students understand a variety of ways to count the number of dots by making equal groups. Discuss what each number in the mathematical expression is representing. For example: • 4 represents the number of sides of the shape because the shape is a square. • 6 is 7 minus 1 and 5 is 7 minus 2.	Let students infer each other's ways of counting and help them see that a mathematical expression can communicate a way of thinking. Help them recall their prior learning, such as the meanings of operations and the order of operations to make sure they can represent their ways of counting correctly.	Do students use operations and the order of operations correctly?
5. Expand Ask students to use a mathematical expression developed when there were only 7 dots on each side of the square to determine the total number of dots there will be when there are 10 dots on each side. Ask a few students if they can find the total number without drawing the shape. Discuss how the mathematical expressions that the class came up with when each side was 7 dots can be used to find the total number of dots when each side is 10 dots.	Encourage students to see which number or numbers in the mathematical expression would be different.	Do students try to use a mathematical expression to find the total number of the dots?
6. Summarizing Help each student identify the learning from the class and record it in their notes. • Mathematical expressions for finding the number of dots for the first problem can be used to find the number of dots in the second problem without drawing and looking at a new diagram.		Does each student summarize their learning and record it in their notes?

Lesson 4: "How Many Sticks Are There Altogether?"

OBJECTIVES

- Students will represent their ways of counting sticks in mathematical expressions and infer other students' ways of counting from their mathematical expressions.
- Students will determine the number of sticks needed to make 30 squares using the mathematical expressions they develop while working on a problem that only has 8 squares.
- Students will confirm that they can use their mathematical expressions to determine the number of sticks even when they cannot count the number of sticks one by one.

LESSON FLOW

Steps, questions from the teacher, activities, and anticipated student responses	Support from the teacher	Check understanding
1. Introduction Let a few students read their journal reflections from Lesson 3 and help the class to recall what they learned.	Before the class, select a few exemplary journal reflections from Lesson 3.	Are students ready for the new problem?
2. Posing the problem Show the diagram and ask the following question: "Using sticks of the same length, we will make squares side by side as shown here. How many sticks do we need to make 8 squares?" *Figure 2.1.1.14*	If students do not understand the situation, guide them to see how the number of sticks increases as the number of squares increase. You can physically demonstrate how the number of squares will increase.	Do students understand the situation?

3. Student problem-solving/anticipated student responses
1. Thinking about how to count.
  (a) Notice that the number of sticks increases by 3 when 1 square is added and write a mathematical expression.
     • $4 + 3 \times 7 = 25$
     • $4 + 3 \times (8 - 1) = 25$
	Let each student write their ways of counting and mathematical expressions in their notes.
	
	Use the seating chart to note each student's way of counting and mathematical expressions to prepare for the whole class discussion.
		Does each student come up with a mathematical expression to represent how to count the number of sticks?

(Continued)

Steps, questions from the teacher, activities, and anticipated student responses	Support from the teacher	Check understanding

(b) Calculating 4×8 because each square has 4 sides and then, since they have been counted twice, subtracting the number of overlapping sticks, 7 (or $8 - 1$), from the product.

- $4 \times 8 - 7 = 25$
- $4 \times 8 - (8 - 1) = 25$

(c) Calculating 8×2 since there are 8 sticks on the top and 8 sticks on the bottom. The number of vertical sticks is $8 + 1$.

- $8 \times 2 + 9 = 25$
- $8 \times 2 + (8 + 1) = 25$

2. Using a drawing of a diagram as the number of squares is increased to explore the number of sticks in relationship to the number of squares.

(a) Notice that the number of sticks increases by 3 when 1 square is added and write a mathematical expression.
- $4 + 3 \times 7 = 25$
- $4 + 3 \times (8 - 1) = 25$
- $1 + 3 \times 8 = 25$

(b) Notice that the number of sticks is increasing by 3 but cannot write a mathematical expression. Results in a misconception such as $4 \times 8 = 32$.

4. Comparison and discussion

For each mathematical expression:

1. Ask one of the students who came up with a mathematical expression to show it to the class.
2. Let the other students infer how they found the number of sticks by interpreting the mathematical expression.
3. Let the student who came up with the mathematical expression explain why that inference is correct or not.

Repeat the above until students understand a variety of ways to find the number of sticks.

Do students understand the different ways to count the number of sticks using the example?

Steps, questions from the teacher, activities, and anticipated student responses	*Support from the teacher*	*Check understanding*
5. Expand Ask students to use a mathematical expression developed when there were 8 squares in the stick diagram to determine the total numbers of sticks there will be when there are 30 squares.	Encourage students to see which number in the mathematical expression would be different.	Do students try to use a mathematical expression to find the total number of sticks?
6. Summarizing Help each student identify the learning from the class and record it in their notes. • The same mathematical expressions for finding the number of sticks for 8 squares can be used to find the number of sticks for various numbers of squares without looking at a diagram.		Does each student summarize their learning and record it in their notes?

Lesson 5: "Summarize and additional exercises"

OBJECTIVES

• Students will become familiar with representing mathematical situations using mathematical expressions by solving practice problems.
• Students will become comfortable solving a problem by recognizing the pattern, representing it with a mathematical expression, and solving it using that mathematical expression.

LESSON FLOW

Review the previous learning from the unit and challenge students with the following practice problems:

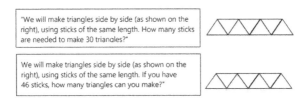

"We will make triangles side by side (as shown on the right), using sticks of the same length. How many sticks are needed to make 30 triangles?"

We will make triangles side by side (as shown on the right), using sticks of the same length. If you have 46 sticks, how many triangles can you make?"

Figure 2.1.1.15

2.1.2 TTP Unit: "Can You Add These Numbers without Counting One by One?"

Grade: Lower elementary

In kindergarten, students developed their number sense by composing and decomposing numbers up to 10. In this unit, students will be introduced to addition of single-digit numbers with sums greater than 10. Students will be encouraged to use their number sense to solve these problems by devising making ten strategies. These making ten strategies will become their foundation for addition involving large-digit numbers and subtractions involving regrouping.

PRIOR LEARNING REQUIRED

- CCSS.Math.Content.K.CC.A.3 "Write numbers from 0 to 20. Represent a number of objects with a written numeral 0-20 (with 0 representing a count of no objects)."
- CCSS.Math.Content.K.OA.A.1 "Represent addition and subtraction with objects, fingers, mental images, drawings, sounds (e.g., claps), acting out situations, verbal explanations, expressions, or equations."
- CCSS.Math.Content.K.OA.A.2 "Solve addition and subtraction word problems, and add and subtract within 10, e.g., by using objects or drawings to represent the problem."
- CCSS.Math.Content.K.OA.A.3 "Decompose numbers less than or equal to 10 into pairs in more than one way."
- CCSS.Math.Content.K.OA.A.4 "For any number from 1 to 9, find the number that makes 10 when added to the given number."
- CCSS.Math.Content.K.NBT.A.1 "Compose and decompose numbers from 11 to 19 into ten ones and some further ones."
- CCSS.Math.Content.1.OA.A.2 "Solve word problems that call for addition of three whole numbers whose sum is less than or equal to 20, e.g., by using objects, drawings, and equations with a symbol for the unknown number to represent the problem."

MAIN CCSS ADDRESSED IN THIS UNIT

- CCSS.Math.Content.1.OA.C.6 (Partial) "Add . . . within 20, demonstrating fluency for addition and subtraction within 10. Use strategies such as counting on; making ten (e.g., $8 + 6 = 8 + 2 + 4 = 10 + 4 = 14$)."

RELATED LATER LEARNING

- CCSS.Math.Content.1.OA.C.6 (Complete) "Add and subtract within 20, demonstrating fluency for addition and subtraction within 10. Use strategies such as counting on; making ten (e.g., $8 + 6 = 8 + 2 + 4 =$

10 + 4 = 14); decomposing a number leading to a ten (e.g., 13 − 4 = 13 −3 − 1 = 10 − 1 = 9); using the relationship between addition and subtraction (e.g., knowing that 8 + 4 = 12, one knows 12 − 8 = 4); and creating equivalent but easier or known sums (e.g., adding 6 + 7 by creating the known equivalent 6 + 6 + 1 = 12 + 1 = 13)."

- CCSS.Math.Content.1.OA.A.1 "Use addition and subtraction within 20 to solve word problems involving situations of adding to, taking from, putting together, taking apart, and comparing, with unknowns in all positions."

The formal study of arithmetic (addition, subtraction, multiplication, and division) typically begins with learning addition. Common Core State Standards introduce basic concepts of addition in kindergarten as the operation to represent add-to and put-together situations. Kindergarteners are expected to understand addition situations and to become adept at adding two one-digit numbers. Developing fluency for the addition of two one-digit numbers is crucial because it is the foundation for all four basic arithmetic calculations. However, asking students to memorize all the addition facts of two one-digit numbers is not an ideal approach to achieving fluency. Instead, teachers need to give students the opportunity to develop calculation strategies.

This unit is designed to help students learn that they can use making ten strategies to add two one-digit numbers with the sums greater than 10 (e.g., 8 + 6 = 8 + 2 + 4 = 10 + 4 = 14). However, students need to be comfortable calculating addition of one-digit numbers with sums less than and equal to ten before they can devise making ten strategies for sums greater than 10. Therefore, before starting this unit, students need to possess a rich number sense of numbers up to ten. They must be able to compose and decompose numbers in various ways. Also, they should know that "twelve" is written as "12" because it consists of ten and two. Once they have this rich number sense regarding numbers up to ten, they are ready for this unit to help them develop making ten strategies for adding two one-digit numbers. Students will experience that in these cases, using a making ten strategy is more reliable than counting on.

This unit is designed based on the most widely used public school mathematics textbook series in Japan, *Atarashii Sansuu* (Hironaka & Sugiyama, 2000), which was published in English as *Mathematics for Elementary School* (Hironaka & Sugiyama, 2006). The lessons incorporate the following key ideas from the textbook:

- The unit begins with an add-to story problem involving 9 + 4, then introduces 8 + 4. Students must devise a making ten strategy by decomposing the second addend in order to solve these problems.
- Students are given ample opportunities to become familiar with the making ten strategy by decomposing the second addend.

- Students will become adept at using making ten strategies in order to prioritize efficiency. For example, they will realize that they can decompose the first addend to make ten for problems such as 3 + 9.
- Students are encouraged to use making ten strategies in order to develop procedural fluency by calculating addition problems such as 5 + 7 and 6 + 6.

In this way, students will become comfortable adding two one-digit numbers with the sums greater than 10.

UNIT FLOW

Lesson	Lesson title and main learning objectives	Time
1	"How can we calculate addition without counting one by one?"	45 min
	Students will realize that addition can be calculated easily if they use their number sense.	
2	"Let's use the making ten strategy to calculate addition (1)"	45 min
	Students will become familiar with the making ten strategy by decomposing the second addend.	
3	"Let's practice addition using the making ten strategy!"	45 min
	Students will develop fluency using the making ten strategy by decomposing the second addend.	
4	"Let's use the making ten strategy to calculate addition (2)"	45 min
	Students will develop fluency using making ten strategies, including decomposing the first addend.	
5	"Let's practice addition using the making ten strategy in different ways! (1)"	45 min
	Students will develop fluency with the making ten strategies by tackling problems in which they must decompose either the first or second addend.	
6	"Let's practice addition using the making ten strategy in different ways! (2)"	45 min
	Students will further develop their fluency with the making ten strategies by tacking problems in which they must decompose either the first or second addend.	

Lesson 1: "How Can We Calculate Addition without Counting One by One?"

OBJECTIVES

- Students will realize that addition can be easily calculated if they use their number sense.

LESSON FLOW

Steps, questions from the teacher, activities, and anticipated student responses	Support from the teacher	Check understanding
1. Introduction Present an addition situation with simple numbers that the students have already studied in the classroom to help them recall that addition can be used to find the total number without counting one by one. For an example, refer to the task below: Ken collected five acorns yesterday and four acorns today. How many acorns does he have now? Ask students to recall how to find the number of acorns without looking at a picture (5 + 4). Let students recall how to compose and decompose numbers up to ten, and that 5 and 4 make 9. You can encourage students to use manipulatives, such as blocks and counters, to check if the answer is correct. Summarize the discussion by writing 5 + 4 = 9 on the board.	Present this as a story problem without showing a picture of the acorns. Encourage students to share their prior knowledge. Help students recall that this is an add-to addition situation, and that if they use a math sentence they do not need to draw pictures of all the acorns and count them.	Do students remember how to use addition to find the number of the acorns?

(Continued)

Steps, questions from the teacher, activities, and anticipated student responses	Support from the teacher	Check understanding

2. Posing the problem

Ask students the following problem:

> Ken collected 9 acorns, and Cindy collected 4 acorns. How many acorns did they collect altogether? How can you find the total number of acorns?

Ask the students if we can use addition to find the total number of acorns.

Support from the teacher:
Have students tackle the problem on their own.

Allow students to use manipulatives or draw pictures only if they ask to do so.

Check understanding:
Does each student understand that they can use addition?

How many students try to add 9 and 4 without drawing a picture or using manipulatives to count them?

3. Student problem-solving/ anticipated student responses

- They recognize that they can use 9 + 4 because this is a put-together addition situation and they can count on from 9 (9, 10, 11, 12, 13) to find the total.
- They recognize that they can use 9 + 4 because this is a put-together addition situation. They find the total number by decomposing 4 into 1 and 3 and make 10 by adding 9 and 1, then add 10 and 3 to find the total (13).

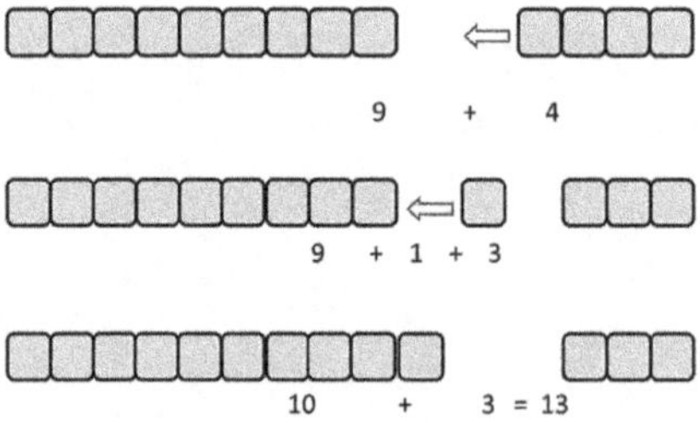

Support from the teacher:
Have each student write down their method in their notes.

Check understanding:
Does each student come up with a way to add 9 + 4?

Figure 2.1.2.01

- They draw groups of 9 and 4 acorns and count on from 9.
- They draw groups of 9 and 4 acorns and count them all one by one, starting from 1.

Steps, questions from the teacher, activities, and anticipated student responses	Support from the teacher	Check understanding
4. Comparison and discussion Ask students to explain their approaches for finding the total number of acorns. Guide students through a whole class discussion to help them understand each other's strategies. Help students understand that addition, 9 + 4, can be used to find the answer because it's a put-together situation. Encourage students to see 9 + 4 can be solved easily if you decompose 4 into 1 and 3 and add the 1 to the 9 to make 10. Let the students try to solve the problem using each other's different methods to make sure they understand all of them.	Write each student's approach on the board so the class can see the similarities and differences. Encourage students to articulate not only how they came up with their answer, but to also say why they used the approach they did. You can give them manipulatives or let them draw on the board to help them visualize their thinking process.	Do students understand how to check if a solution method makes sense? Do they understand all the solution methods?
5. Summarizing Help each student identify the learning from the class and record it in their notes. • We can use addition to solve this problem. • We can add 9 and 4 by breaking down 4 into 1 and 3, and add the 1 to 9 to make 10. Then we can add 10 and 3 to find the total number 13. • Even when the numbers are larger, we can still add them without counting one by one.		Does every student write down the summary in their notes?

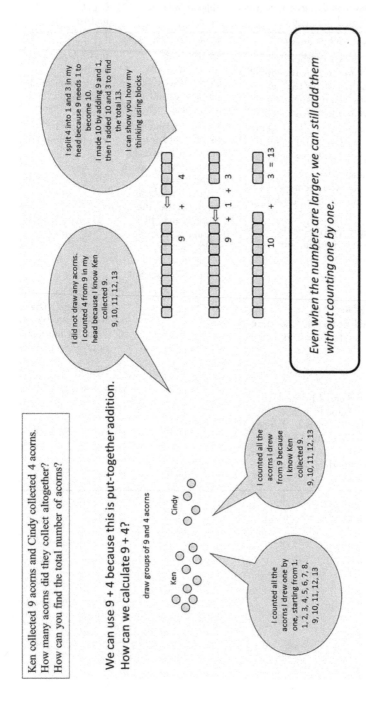

Figure 2.1.2.02 Neriage Map for Lesson 1: "How can we calculate addition without counting one by one?"

Lesson 2: "Let's Use the Making Ten Strategy to Calculate Addition (1)"

OBJECTIVES

- Students will become familiar with the making ten strategy by decomposing the second addend.

LESSON FLOW

Steps, questions from the teacher, activities, and anticipated student responses	Support from the teacher	Check understanding
1. Introduction Ask some students to share what they wrote in their notebook in the previous lesson to help the class recall what they learned. • We can use addition to solve this problem. • We can add 9 and 4 by breaking down 4 into 1 and 3, and add the 1 to 9 to make 10. Then we can add 10 and 3 to find the total number 13. • Even when the numbers are larger, we can still add them without counting one by one. Introduce the calculation strategy above as the "making ten strategy" and let each student try using manipulatives, such as counting blocks, to practice using this strategy.	Select some examples from students' notebooks describing strategies to calculate 9 + 4 and share them with the class. Let each student use manipulatives to experience decomposing 4 into 1 and 3, and then combining 9 and 1 to make 10. After each student completes the manipulation on their own, let students work with partners to make sure they all understand how to use the making ten strategy for 9 + 4.	Does each student understand the making ten strategy?

(Continued)

Steps, questions from the teacher, activities, and anticipated student responses	Support from the teacher	Check understanding
2. Apply the learning to a similar situation Ask students to use the making ten strategy to calculate other addition problems such as the one below: Let's calculate 9 + 3 using the making ten strategy. First, have each student try to find the sum on their own using the making ten strategy and without using manipulatives. Then, have students make pairs and explain to each other how to calculate the problem using manipulatives.	Let students use manipulatives if they are struggling on their own.	Does each student try to use the making ten strategy?
3. Student problem-solving/anticipated student responses • Add 9 and 3 by decomposing 3 into 1 and 2, add the 1 to 9 to make 10, and then add the 2 to 10 to make 12. 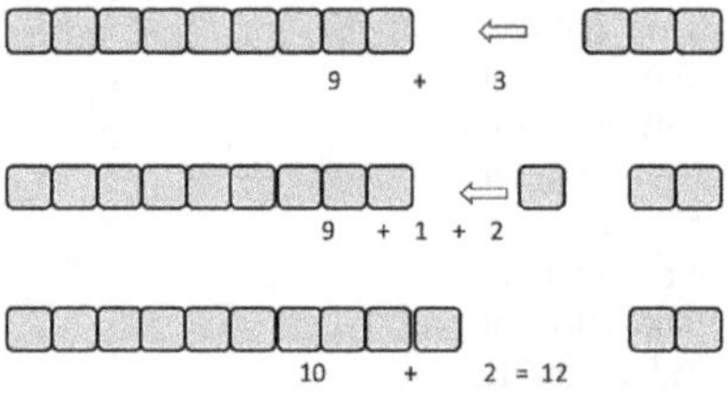	Have each student write down their method in their notebook.	Does each student come up with a way to use a making ten strategy to add 9 + 3?

Figure 2.1.2.03

4. Comparison and discussion Guide students through a class discussion to help them understand that the making ten strategy they used in the previous lesson can also be used to calculate 9 + 3. Encourage them to try using making ten to perform other addition calculations.		Does each student understand how to use the making ten strategy?

Steps, questions from the teacher, activities, and anticipated student responses	Support from the teacher	Check understanding
5. Apply the learning to another situation Ask students the following problem:	Let students use manipulatives if they are struggling on their own.	Does each student try to use the making ten strategy?

> Let's use the making ten strategy to do other addition problems. Let's calculate 8 + 3.

First, have each student try to find the sum on their own using making ten and without using manipulatives.

Then, have students make pairs and explain to each other how to calculate the problem using manipulatives.

6. Student problem-solving/anticipated student responses • Add 8 and 3 by decomposing 3 into 2 and 1, add the 2 to 8 to make 10, and then add the 1 to 10 to find the total of 11. 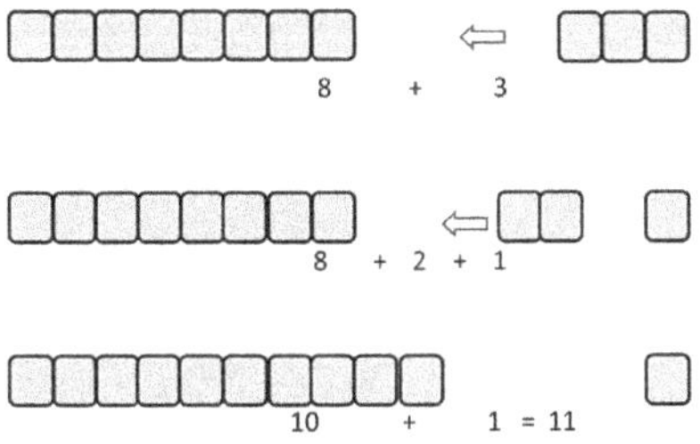	Have each student write down their method in their notebook.	Does each student come up with a way to use a making ten strategy to add 8 + 3?

Figure 2.1.2.04

7. Comparison and discussion Help students understand that the making ten strategy can also be used to calculate 8 + 3.	Make sure the students understand how to apply the making ten strategy to 8 + 3 and encourage them to try other additions.	Does each student understand how to use the making ten strategy?

8. Summarizing

Help each student identify the learning from the class and record it in their notes.

• We can use making ten to add 9 + 3 and 8 + 3 easily.

Lesson 3: "Let's Practice Addition Using the Making Ten Strategy!"

OBJECTIVES

• Students will develop fluency with the making ten strategy by decomposing the second addend.

INSTRUCTION

• This is an exercise lesson. Students will deepen their understanding of the making ten strategy and become comfortable decomposing the second addend to make ten by calculating many different addition problems, such as: $9 + 5, 9 + 6, 9 + 7, 9 + 8, 8 + 4, 8 + 5, 8 + 6, 8 + 7, 8 + 8, 7 + 4, 7 + 5,$ and $7 + 6$.
• Help students deepen their understanding of addition situations by giving them story problems that require them to decompose the second addend to make ten.
• Let students work with partners to check if their calculations are correct.

Lesson 4: "Let's Use The Making Ten Strategy to Calculate Addition (2)"

OBJECTIVES

• Students will become adept at using making ten strategies, including decomposing the first addend.

LESSON FLOW

Steps, questions from the teacher, activities, and anticipated student responses	Support from the teacher	Check understanding
1. Introduction Ask some students to share what they wrote in their notebook in the previous lessons to help the class recall what they have learned. • Addition problems like $9 + 4$ can be calculated using making ten. • We can break down 4 into 1 and 3, and add 1 to 9 to make 10. Then we add 10 and 3 to find the total number 13.	Select some examples from the students' notebooks which describe making ten and share them with the class.	Does each student recall the process of making ten?

Steps, questions from the teacher, activities, and anticipated student responses	Support from the teacher	Check understanding
2. Posing the problem Ask students the following problem:	Let students use manipulatives if they are struggling.	Does each student try to apply the making ten strategy?

> 3 white flowers and 9 yellow flowers are in bloom. How many flowers are in bloom altogether? Think about how you can solve this problem and write down your idea using a math sentence.

Let students share the math sentence (3 + 9) and ask them to explain why this problem can be solved using addition.

> Do you think you can use the making ten strategy for this addition problem?
> Is this different from other addition problems that we have solved using the making ten strategy?

Ask students to share their reasoning.

3. Student problem-solving/anticipated student responses • Add 3 and 9 by decomposing 9 into 7 and 2, add the 7 to 3 to make 10, and then add the 2 to 10 to find the total of 12. 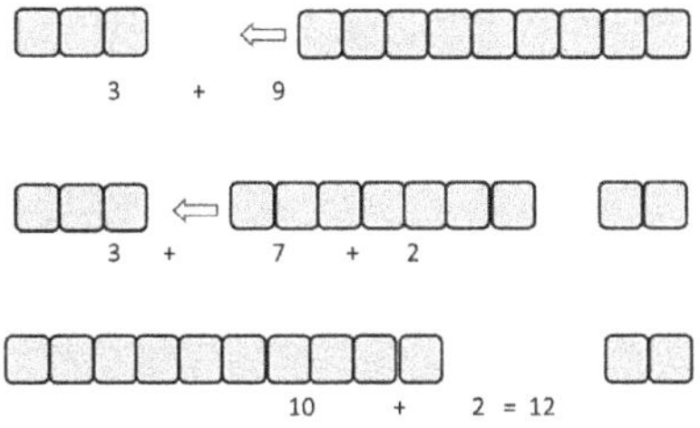	Have each student write down their method in their notebook.	Does each student come up with a way to use a making ten strategy to add 3 + 9?

Figure 2.1.2.05

(Continued)

Steps, questions from the teacher, activities, and anticipated student responses	Support from the teacher	Check understanding

- Add 3 and 9 by decomposing 3 into 1 and 2, add the 1 to 9 to make 10, and then add the 2 to 10 to find the total of 12.

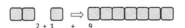

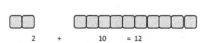

Figure 2.1.2.06

4. Comparison and discussion

Lead a whole class discussion to examine the similarities and differences between students' strategies.

Identify that both making ten strategies (shown above in "Anticipated student responses") try to make 10 but in different ways. One approach makes 10 from 3 by decomposing 9 into 7 and 2 and the other makes 10 from 9 by decomposing 3 into 1 and 2.

Help students understand that you can make 10 from the number you feel the most comfortable using.

Let students try using each other's ways of making ten (decomposing the first or second addend) to see which method they prefer.

Make sure the students understand the different ways they can use the making ten strategy to add 3 + 9 and encourage them to try the method of making ten that they didn't choose for themselves during "Pose the problem."

Does each student understand the different ways they can use making ten?

5. Apply the learning to another situation

Ask students the following problem:

> Let's use making ten to do other addition problems. Let's add 6 + 7 using making ten.

First, have students work on their own without using manipulatives.

Then, have students make pairs and explain their method to their partner using manipulatives.

Let students use manipulatives if they are struggling on their own.

Does each student try to apply making ten?

Steps, questions from the teacher, activities, and anticipated student responses	Support from the teacher	Check understanding
6. Student problem-solving/anticipated student responses • Add 6 and 7 by decomposing 7 into 4 and 3, add the 4 to 6 to make 10, and then add the 3 to 10 to find the total of 13.	Have each student write down their method in their notebook.	Does each student come up with a way to use a making ten strategy to add 6 + 7?

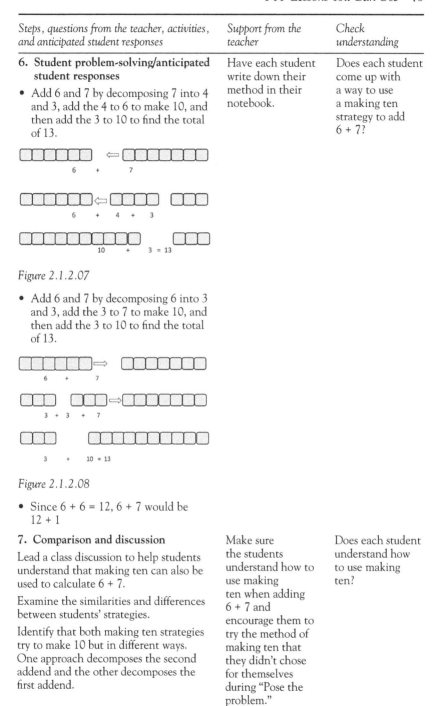

Figure 2.1.2.07

• Add 6 and 7 by decomposing 6 into 3 and 3, add the 3 to 7 to make 10, and then add the 3 to 10 to find the total of 13.

Figure 2.1.2.08

• Since 6 + 6 = 12, 6 + 7 would be 12 + 1

7. Comparison and discussion Lead a class discussion to help students understand that making ten can also be used to calculate 6 + 7. Examine the similarities and differences between students' strategies. Identify that both making ten strategies try to make 10 but in different ways. One approach decomposes the second addend and the other decomposes the first addend.	Make sure the students understand how to use making ten when adding 6 + 7 and encourage them to try the method of making ten that they didn't chose for themselves during "Pose the problem."	Does each student understand how to use making ten?

(Continued)

Steps, questions from the teacher, activities, and anticipated student responses	Support from the teacher	Check understanding
Help students understand that you can make 10 from the number that you feel the most comfortable using. Let students try using each other's ways of making ten (decomposing the first or second addend) to see which method they prefer.	Some students may come up with the approach 6 + 6 = 12. Help students see how doubling 6 can be useful to find 6 + 7.	

8. Summarizing

Help each student identify the learning from the class and record it in their notes.

- Even addition problems like 3 + 9 and 6 + 7 can be calculated easily by using making ten.
- You can choose which way to make 10 based on your preference.

Lessons 5 and 6: "Let's Practice Addition Using the Making Ten Strategy in Different Ways!"

OBJECTIVES

- Students will further develop their fluency with the making ten strategies by tackling problems in which they must decompose either the first or second addend.

INSTRUCTION

- These are exercise lessons. Students will deepen their understanding of making ten and become confident decomposing either the first or second addend by calculating addition problems with sums greater than 10, such as: 2 + 9, 3 + 8, 4 + 7, 5 + 6, 5 + 8, 6 + 8, 8 + 9, 7 + 7, and 7 + 8.
- Help students deepen their understanding of addition situations by giving them story problems in which they must decompose either the first or second addend.
- Let students work with partners to check if their calculations are correct.

2.1.3 TTP Unit: *"Ideas for Quantifying Crowdedness and Speed"*

Grade: Lower secondary level

The first lesson in this unit asks students to come up with their own ideas for comparing quantities using two independent measurements, the number of people in three rooms and the size of each room. In the following two lessons, this concept is expanded upon to include comparing population densities and speeds. This mini unit is designed to build on what students have learned about measurements and multiplicative comparisons in the elementary grades and gives them the foundation they will need to further investigate rates and ratios.

PRIOR LEARNING REQUIRED

- CCSS.Math.Content.4.OA.A.2 "Multiply or divide to solve word problems involving multiplicative comparison, e.g., by using drawings and equations with a symbol for the unknown number to represent the problem, distinguishing multiplicative comparison from additive comparison."
- CCSS.Math.Content.5.NBT.B.7 "Add, subtract, multiply, and divide decimals to hundredths, using concrete models or drawings and strategies based on place value, properties of operations, and/or the relationship between addition and subtraction; relate the strategy to a written method and explain the reasoning used."

MAIN CCSS ADDRESSED IN THIS UNIT

- CCSS.Math.Content.6.RP.A.2 (Partial) "Understand the concept of a unit rate a/b associated with a ratio a : b with b≠0, and use rate language in the context of a ratio relationship."
- CCSS.Math.Content.6.RP.A.3 (Partial) "Use ratio and rate reasoning to solve real-world and mathematical problems, e.g., by reasoning about tables of equivalent ratios, tape diagrams, double number line diagrams, or equations."

RELATED LATER LEARNING

- CCSS.Math.Content.6.RP.A.2 (Complete) "Understand the concept of a unit rate a/b associated with a ratio a : b with b≠0, and use rate language in the context of a ratio relationship."
- CCSS.Math.Content.6.RP.A.3 (Complete) "Use ratio and rate reasoning to solve real-world and mathematical problems, e.g., by reasoning about tables of equivalent ratios, tape diagrams, double number line diagrams, or equations."

- CCSS.Math.Content.6.EE.C.9 Use variables to represent two quantities in a real-world problem that change in relationship to one another; write an equation to express one quantity, thought of as the dependent variable, in terms of the other quantity, thought of as the independent variable. Analyze the relationship between the dependent and independent variables using graphs and tables, and relate these to the equation. For example, in a problem involving motion at constant speed, list and graph ordered pairs of distances and times, and write the equation d = 65t to represent the relationship between distance and time.

CCSS dictate that sixth graders should be able to work with unit rates, however, this is one of the most challenging topics covered in the middle school grades (2010). Students have already learned how to use units to make simple comparisons of quantities, such as lengths in the second grade and liquid volumes and masses in the third grade (Common Core State Standards Initiative, 2010). The lessons in this unit build upon this experience, giving students problem situations in which they must measure two different kinds of quantities in order to create and compare unit rates. For example, in order to quantify the crowdedness of various rooms, they must look at both the sizes of each room as well as the number of people in them. Students will realize that some comparisons, such as crowdedness and speed, cannot be quantified using only a single measurement, underscoring the importance of ratios and unit rates.

One of the reasons that students find ratios, rates, and proportional relationships so challenging is that they don't realize how they relate to what they have already studied in elementary school. CCSS introduce the foundation of proportional relationships in the third grade, when students learn to use multiplication and division as operations which represent situations involving equal groups (2010). In the fourth grade, they encounter multiplicative comparison (Common Core State Standards Initiative, 2010). The three lessons in this unit are based on the Japanese mathematics textbook *Atarashii Sansuu* (Fujii & Majima, 2020a), and introduce ratios and rates as a natural extension of the multiplication and division situations with which students are already familiar. These lessons guide students to work out on their own why they need unit rates and how to create and use them, bridging the gap between their prior learning and this challenging topic.

The first lesson opens with a problem situation that relates to students' everyday lives, asking them to find which of three rooms is the most crowded. However, one of the unique aspects of this problem situation is that students are not given all the information they need to solve the problem at first. The number of students in each cabin, but not the size of each room is provided. This is intentional. Students are expected to realize through discussion that they also need to know the size of each room in order to figure out how crowded each room is. The second lesson expands upon this concept to include the idea of population density. In the third lesson, students must compare different speeds, requiring them to look at both time and distance in order to quantify the rates. Through the discussions in these three lessons, students will solidify their understanding of rates. Once students complete this unit, they should be given a variety of real-life problem situations so that they can become comfortable working with ratios, rates, and proportional relationships.

UNIT FLOW

Lesson	Lesson title and main learning objectives	Time
1	"How can we find out which room is the most crowded?"	60 min
	Students will realize that in order to compare the crowdedness of three rooms they need to know the number of people in each room as well as the size. They will then devise and discuss ways to quantify crowdedness in order to find out which room is the most crowded.	
2	"Population density"	60 min
	Students will understand why people use population density, the number of people divided by the area, to quantify crowdedness.	
3	"How can we compare speeds?"	60 min
	Students will realize that time and distance are needed to compare speeds. Students will understand why we use kilometers/miles per hour to quantify the speed of vehicles.	
4	"Let's use the ideas that we learned to solve more problem!"	60 min
	Students will become comfortable using idea of per unit quantities to solve various problems.	

Lesson 1: "How Can We Find Out which Room is the Most Crowded?"

OBJECTIVES

- Students will realize that in order to find which room is the most crowded they need to know the number of people in each room as well as the size.
- Students will devise and discuss ways to quantify crowdedness to find out which room is the most crowded.

LESSON FLOW

Steps, questions from the teacher, activities, and anticipated student responses	Support from the teacher	Check understanding
1. Introduction Show the illustration of cabin rooms at summer camp and ask the following question: Which one of the three rooms is the most crowded?	Encourage students to share their opinions. Encourage them to share what they think "crowdedness" means.	Is each student comfortable using the term "crowdedness"?

Cabin Room A **Cabin Room B**   **Cabin Room C**

Figure 2.1.3.01

Lead a class discussion on how to find out which room is the most crowded:

- Room A is more crowded than Room B because Room A has more people in the same size room.
- Room B and Room C have the same number of people but we can't tell which room is more crowded. If Room B is larger than Room C, then Room C is more crowded. We need to know the size (area) of each room in order to compare the crowdedness of the rooms.

Help students realize that the information given in the problem may not be enough to decide which room is the most crowded. Knowing the size (area) of each room is essential to determine which room is the most crowded.

Steps, questions from the teacher, activities, and anticipated student responses	*Support from the teacher*	*Check understanding*
2. Posing the problem Show students the table in Figure 2.1.3.02 and give them the following problem: This table shows information about Room A, Room B, and Room C. Determine which room is the most crowded using this information.	Have students work individually. Help students see that Rooms A and B can be easily compared by looking at the number of people in each room because the sizes of both rooms are the same. Help students see that Rooms B and C can be easily compared by looking at the size of each room because both rooms have the same number of people.	Does each student understand that Room B is less crowded than both Room A and Room C, but that it is not easy to determine whether Room A or Room C is more crowded?

	Number of People	Size of the Room (m²)
Room A	6	16
Room B	5	16
Room C	5	15

Figure 2.1.3.02

Help students realize that by looking at the table they can determine that Room B is the least crowded room.

Help students realize that comparing the crowdedness of Room A and Room C is the challenge because both the numbers of the students and the sizes of the rooms are different.

Let's find out how to compare the crowdedness of Room A and Room C.

(Continued)

Steps, questions from the teacher, activities, and anticipated student responses	Support from the teacher	Check understanding
3. Student problem-solving/ anticipated student responses a) Room A: $16 \div 6 = 2.66$ $(m^2) \div (people) = (m^2 \text{ per person})$ Room C: $15 \div 5 = 3$ $(m^2) \div (people) = (m^2 \text{ per person})$ Therefore, Room A is more crowded than Room C. b) Room A: $6 \div 16 = 0.375$ $(people) \div (m^2) = (people \text{ per } m^2)$ Room C: $5 \div 15 = 0.33$ $(people) \div (m^2) = (people \text{ per } m^2)$ Therefore, Room A is more crowded than Room C. c) The LCM (least common multiple) of 16 and 15 is 240. Room A: $6 \times 15 = 90$ Room C: $5 \times 16 = 80$ Therefore, Room A is more crowded than Room C. d) The LCM of 6 and 5 is 30 Room A: $16 \times 5 = 80$ Room C: $15 \times 6 = 90$ Therefore, Room A is more crowded than Room C.	Have each student write their way of expressing the fractional part in their notes.	Does each student come up with a way to represent the fractional part?

Steps, questions from the teacher, activities, and anticipated student responses	Support from the teacher	Check understanding
4. Comparison and discussion Compare and discuss each students' approach, so that they understand each other's methods. Help students understand why Room B is the least crowded and why it was a challenge to identify whether Room A or Room C was more crowded. Lead a whole class discussion to understand the idea behind each solution method: a) Compares how much space (m²) each person has. b) Compares how many people there are in each 1 m² space. c) Compares how many people there would be in each room if the sizes of both rooms were the same (240 m²). d) Compares how big each room would be if the number of people in each room was the same (30 people).	Lead a whole class discussion to help students see that solution methods a) and b) may be the most reliable because they use division to find unit quantities.	Does each student understand the idea behind each approach?
5. Summarizing Help each student identify the learning from the class and record it in their notes. • Crowdedness can be compared using two measurements, the number of people in the space and the size of the space (area). • There are several different approaches that can be used to quantify crowdedness.		Does every student write down the summary in their notes?

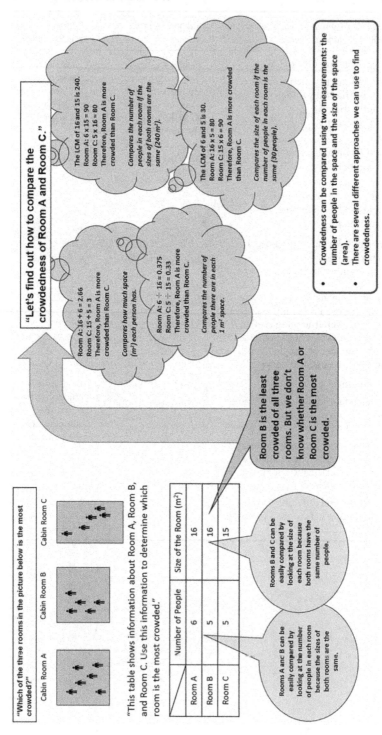

Figure 2.1.3.03 *Neriage Map for Lesson 1: "How can we find out which room is the most crowded?"*

Lesson 2: "Population Density"

OBJECTIVES

- Students will understand why people use population density, the number of people divided by the area, to quantify crowdedness.

LESSON FLOW

Steps, questions from the teacher, activities, and anticipated student responses	Support from the teacher	Check understanding
1. Introduction Ask some students to share what they wrote in their notebook in the previous lesson to help the class recall what they learned. • Crowdedness can be compared using two measurements, the number of people in the space and the size of the space (area). • There are several different approaches that can be used to quantify crowdedness.	Show the table used during the previous lesson.	Does every student remember the two approaches that use division to find unit quantities?
2. Posing the problem Show the table and give students the following problem: This table shows information about City A and City B. Use the data to determine which city is more crowded. |	Population	Area (km²)
City A	11,980,000	16,800
City B	2,240,000	2,880		Have students work individually. Allow students to use a calculator. Let students realize that using LCM may be difficult because the numbers are too large.	Does each student figure out they can use division to find the unit rates?
3. Student problem-solving/anticipated student responses a) City A: $11,980,000 \div 16,800 = 713.09$ (people) $\div$ (km²) = (people per km²) City B: $2,240,000 \div 2,880 = 777.77$ (people) $\div$ (km²) = (people per km²) Therefore, City B is more crowded than City A. b) City A: $16,800 \div 11,980,000 = 0.0014$ (km²) $\div$ (people) = (km² per person) City B: $2,880 \div 2,240,000 = 0.0012$ (km²) $\div$ (people) = (km² per person) Therefore, City B is more crowded than City A.	Make sure each student is ready to explain how to interpret the numbers they obtained from their division calculations.	Can each student explain the meaning of the numbers in the division calculations?

(Continued)

Steps, questions from the teacher, activities, and anticipated student responses	*Support from the teacher*	*Check understanding*
4. Comparison and discussion Lead a whole class discussion to help students understand the idea behind each solution method: a) The number of people who have to share a 1 km² space (people per km²). b) How many km² each person has to themselves (km² per person). We often compare the crowdedness of cities and countries by finding the number of people per km². We call this "population density" (*number of people ÷ area*). Why do you think we use this calculation and not *area ÷ number of people*?	Help students realize that when you calculate population density by *number of people ÷ area*, the city with the larger number is more crowded. However, when you calculate the population density by *area ÷ number of people*, the city with the smaller number is more crowded. Help students realize that it may be easier to compare the crowdedness of cities by calculating the *number of people ÷ area* (population density) for each city.	Does each student understand the new term "population density"?
5. Apply the learning to another situation Show the table and give students the following problem: This table shows information about City A, City B, and City C. Use the data to determine which city is the most crowded and which city is the second most crowded. <table><tr><td></td><td>Population</td><td>Area (km²)</td></tr><tr><td>City A</td><td>1,900,000</td><td>1,120</td></tr><tr><td>City B</td><td>1,000,000</td><td>780</td></tr><tr><td>City C</td><td>1,400,000</td><td>340</td></tr></table>	Have students work individually. Allow students to use a calculator. Encourage students to use population density to compare the crowdedness of the cities.	Does every student understand how to calculate the population density and how to interpret the results?
6. Summarizing • Crowdedness can be compared using division to find unit rates. • We compare the crowdedness of cities and countries by finding the number of people per km². We call this "population density" (number of people ÷ area).		Does every student write down the summary in their notes?

Lesson 3: "How Can We Compare Speeds?"

OBJECTIVES

• Students will realize that time and distance are needed to compare speeds. Students will understand why we use kilometers per hour to quantify the speed of vehicles.

LESSON FLOW

Steps, questions from the teacher, activities, and anticipated student responses	Support from the teacher	Check understanding
1. Introduction Ask some students to share what they wrote in their notebook in the previous lesson to help the class recall what they learned. • Crowdedness can be compared using division to find unit rates. • We compare the crowdedness of cities and countries by finding the number of people per km². We call this "population density" (number of people ÷ area). Present students with the following task:	Help students realize that only knowing how long it took for each train to reach its destination may not be enough to compare the speeds because the trains may have traveled different distances. Help students realize that we need to know how far each train traveled as well as how long it took to get there in order to find and compare the speeds.	Does each student understand the problem situation?

A high-speed train T travels from City A to City B in 3 hours. Another high-speed train P travels from City C to City D in 2 hours. Which traveled faster, Train T or Train P?

Help students discuss if the information given is enough to determine which train traveled faster.

Help students realize that they need to know the distance between City A and City B and the distance between City C and City D in order to determine which train traveled faster.

(Continued)

Steps, questions from the teacher, activities, and anticipated student responses	Support from the teacher	Check understanding
2. Posing the problem Present students with the following task:	Have students work individually.	Does each student apply the concept of unit quantities?

> A high-speed train T travels from City A to City B in 3 hours. The distance between City A and City B is 660 km. Another high-speed train P travels from City C to City D in 2 hours. The distance between City C and City D is 420 km. Which traveled faster, Train T or Train P?

3. Student problem-solving/ anticipated student responses a) Train T: $660 \div 3 = 220$ (km) ÷ (hours) = (km per hour) Train P: $420 \div 2 = 210$ (km) ÷ (hours) = (km per hour) Therefore, Train T is faster than Train P. b) Train T: $3 \div 660 = 0.0045$ (hours) ÷ (km) = (hours spent traveling per km) Train P: $2 \div 420 = 0.0047$ (hours) ÷ (km) = (hours spent traveling per km) Therefore, Train T is faster than Train P.	Make sure each student is ready to explain how to interpret the numbers they obtained from their division calculations.	Can each student explain the meaning of the numbers in the division calculations?
4. Comparison and discussion Lead a whole class discussion to help students understand the ideas behind each solution method. a) The distance the train traveled each hour (km per hour). b) The time the train needed to travel 1 km (how long it took to travel 1 km).	Help students understand the idea of kilometers/ miles per hour. Help students realize that when you calculate speed by distance ÷ hours, the train with the larger number is faster.	Does each student understand how to compare speeds?

Steps, questions from the teacher, activities, and anticipated student responses	Support from the teacher	Check understanding
We often compare the speeds of trains and cars by finding the distance traveled per hour. We call this "kilometers/miles per hour" (distance ÷ hours). Why do you think we use this calculation and not hours ÷ distance?	However, when you calculate the speed by hours ÷ distance, the train with the smaller number is faster. Help students realize that it may be easier to compare speeds by calculating the distance ÷ hours (kilometers per hour) for each train.	
5. Apply the learning to another situation Show the table and give students the following problem:	Allow students to use a calculator. Encourage students to come up with several different ways to find the speed. Help students realize the unit of time doesn't have to be 1 hour. It could also be 1 minute.	Does every student understand how to calculate the speeds and interpret the results?

This table shows information about Car A, Car B, and Car C. Use the data to determine which car was the fastest and which car was the second fastest.

	Time traveled	Distance (km) traveled
Car A	1 hour 20 minutes	80
Car B	2 hours	110
Car C	50 minutes	60

Help students discuss their solution methods as a class.

6. Summarizing

Help each student identify the learning from the class and record it in their notes.

- Speed can be compared using division to find the unit rates.

Does every student write down the summary in their notes?

Lesson 4: "Let's Use the Ideas We Learned to Solve More Problems!"

OBJECTIVES

• Students will become comfortable using per unit quantities to solve various problems.

INSTRUCTION

• This is an exercise lesson. Students will deepen their understanding of per unit quantities by solving various problems, such as:

  (a) Car A traveled 300 miles using 15 gallons of gasoline. Car B traveled 400 miles using 25 gallons of gasoline. Which car can travel more miles on 1 gallon of gasoline?
  (b) Which notepad is more expensive, one that is part of a 12-pack for 30 dollars or one that is part of a 10-pack for 23 dollars?
  (c) There is a wire that weighs 8 grams per meter. This wire was used to create a 49.6 gram piece of art. How many meters of wire were used?

2.1.4 TTP Unit: "Deriving the Area Formula of a Parallelogram"

Grade: Upper elementary or lower secondary

This unit will challenge students to create a formula for finding the area of a parallelogram. They will examine the difference between finding the area of a rectangle and a parallelogram. This will help them develop a deeper understanding of the formula itself as well as its two essential measurements, base and height. Students will also be given the opportunity to apply the area formula for parallelograms to a variety of situations until they become comfortable using it. This experience will prepare them in the future to derive area formulas for other shapes such as triangles, trapezoids, and rhombuses.

PRIOR LEARNING REQUIRED

• CCSS.Math.Content.3.MD.C.5 "Recognize area as an attribute of plane figures and understand concepts of area measurement."
• CCSS.Math.Content.3.MD.C.6 "Measure areas by counting unit squares (square cm, square m, square in, square ft, and improvised units)."
• CCSS.Math.Content.3.MD.C.7 "Relate area to the operations of multiplication and addition."

  • CCSS.Math.Content.3.MD.C.7.A "Find the area of a rectangle with whole-number side lengths by tiling it, and show that the area is the same as would be found by multiplying the side lengths."

- CCSS.Math.Content.3.MD.C.7.B "Multiply side lengths to find areas of rectangles with whole-number side lengths in the context of solving real world and mathematical problems, and represent whole-number products as rectangular areas in mathematical reasoning."
- CCSS.Math.Content.3.MD.C.7.C "Use tiling to show in a concrete case that the area of a rectangle with whole-number side lengths a and $b + c$ is the sum of $a \times b$ and $a \times c$. Use area models to represent the distributive property in mathematical reasoning."
- CCSS.Math.Content.3.MD.C.7.D "Recognize area as additive. Find areas of rectilinear figures by decomposing them into non-overlapping rectangles and adding the areas of the non-overlapping parts, applying this technique to solve real world problems."

- CCSS.Math.Content.3.MD.D.8 "Solve real world and mathematical problems involving perimeters of polygons, including finding the perimeter given the side lengths, finding an unknown side length, and exhibiting rectangles with the same perimeter and different areas or with the same area and different perimeters."
- CCSS.Math.Content.3.G.A.1 "Understand that shapes in different categories (e.g., rhombuses, rectangles, and others) may share attributes (e.g., having four sides), and that the shared attributes can define a larger category (e.g., quadrilaterals). Recognize rhombuses, rectangles, and squares as examples of quadrilaterals, and draw examples of quadrilaterals that do not belong to any of these subcategories."
- CCSS.Math.Content.4.G.A.1 "Draw points, lines, line segments, rays, angles (right, acute, obtuse) and perpendicular and parallel lines. Identify these in two-dimensional figures."
- CCSS.Math.Content.4.G.A.2 "Classify two-dimensional figures based on the presence or absence of parallel or perpendicular lines, or the presence or absence of angles of a specified size. Recognize right triangles as a category, and identify right triangles."
- CCSS.Math.Content.5.G.B.3 "Understand that attributes belonging to a category of two dimensional figures also belong to all subcategories of that category."
- CCSS.Math.Content.5.G.B.4 "Classify two-dimensional figures in a hierarchy based on properties."

MAIN CCSS ADDRESSED IN THIS UNIT

- CCSS.Math.Content.6.G.A.1 (Partial) "Find the area of right triangles, other triangles, special quadrilaterals, and polygons by composing into rectangles or decomposing into triangles and other shapes; apply these techniques in the context of solving real-world and mathematical problems."

RELATED LATER LEARNING

- CCSS.Math.Content.6.G.A.1 (Complete) "Find the area of right triangles, other triangles, special quadrilaterals, and polygons by composing into rectangles or decomposing into triangles and other shapes; apply these techniques in the context of solving real-world and mathematical problems."
- CCSS.Math.Content.7.G.B.4 "Know the formulas for the area and circumference of a circle and use them to solve problems; give an informal derivation of the relationship between the circumference and area of a circle."
- CCSS.Math.Content.7.G.B.6 "Solve real-world and mathematical problems involving area, volume and surface area of two- and three-dimensional objects composed of triangles, quadrilaterals, polygons, cubes, and right prisms."

This unit introduces the concept of finding the area of a parallelogram by building on students' knowledge of the area formula for rectangles. Students are asked if the area of a rectangle shown tilting into a parallelogram changes or stays the same. By closely examining the relationship between a rectangle and a parallelogram with the same perimeters, they will discover how they can find the area of a parallelogram by rearranging it into a rectangle and by counting the unit squares. These strategies can be challenging, but discussing each other's solution methods as a class will address any misunderstandings students may have. The various problems and discussions in each lesson provide opportunities for them to realize that they can find the area of a parallelogram by multiplying the base by the height. This will cement their understanding of both the usefulness and meaning of the area formula, preparing them to be able to devise new formulas for other shapes in the future.

This unit re-visits the idea of unit squares, as students may have difficulty understanding how they relate to area formulas. I have observed that even though sixth grade students already learned how to measure the area of rectangles and squares by devising the formulas in the third grade, they have difficulty using this concept to develop formulas for finding the area of parallelograms, triangles, trapezoids, and rhombuses. They will still try to draw and count the unit squares one by one. Furthermore, many sixth graders still can't use area formulas even after they have been taught them. Instead, they continue to try to solve problems by drawing and counting unit squares. This is because they don't fully understand how they can use multiplication to find the number of unit squares in a geometric shape. To address this issue, the first lesson in this unit opens with a review of how we derived the area formula for a rectangle by counting and multiplying unit squares, making sure students understand this essential concept.

This unit shows how a parallelogram can be decomposed and rearranged into a rectangle to help students understand how they can find the area of a parallelogram. CCSS dictate that one of the primary goals for sixth and seventh graders is learning how to find the area of triangles, special quadrilaterals, and polygons by composing or decomposing them into other shapes (Common Core State Standards Initiative, 2010). However, CCSS do not specify how students can use their prior learning to figure this out on their own. The Japanese curriculum (e.g., Fujii & Majima, 2020a) suggests the following three strategies:

1   Students can decompose a geometrical figure into a few parts and rearrange those parts into a shape with which they are already familiar (equivalent-area transformation).
2   Students can think about a given shape as half the area of a geometrical figure for which they already know how to find the area. They can find the area of the familiar geometric figure and then divide it in half (doubling a shape).
3   Students can decompose a shape into several geometrical figures for which they already know how to find the areas, calculate each of those, and then add them all together (decomposing a shape).

These strategies can help students understand the concept of area more deeply, which in turn will help them figure out the formulas for the area of new shapes. This unit uses the equivalent-area transformation strategy to help students see the relationship between parallelograms and rectangles.

Furthermore, American students typically learn the area formulas for rectangles and parallelograms separately. Most mathematics textbooks available in the U.S. briefly address the relationship between the area formulas for rectangles and parallelograms by showing a diagram of a parallelogram being converted into a rectangle. However, a single diagram often doesn't provide enough context for most students. It is not clear to them why the area of rectangles can be found by multiplying two adjacent sides, but why this is not the case for parallelograms. This unit suggests using software to show the transformation of a rectangle into a parallelogram, along with an in-depth discussion of how the area of the shape changes as it becomes more slanted, even though its perimeter measurements stay the same. This makes it clear why we cannot multiply adjacent sides of a parallelogram to find the area. It also provides an opportunity to discuss the terms "base" and "height."

We want students to understand why we need the base and height, not the two adjacent sides, in order to find the area of a parallelogram. This unit reviews the formula for finding the area of rectangles, because any misunderstanding of this formula, especially the concepts of base and height, will be an obstacle for students trying to understand the formula for finding the area of parallelograms. For example, students often struggle to calculate the area of a parallelogram such as Figure 2.1.4.01, a problem commonly used in Japanese mathematics textbooks for grade 5 in elementary school (e.g., Fujii & Majima, 2020b), even though they know the area formula is base times height. This is because three measurements are given, including an unnecessary one, and they struggle to identify which two are the ones they need. It's also not immediately clear which measurements could be the base or height, because the parallelogram is not presented lying flat. Students will have to work with this figure in Lesson 2 of this unit, addressing any misconceptions they may still have regarding area, and preparing them to work with a variety of parallelograms in Lesson 3.

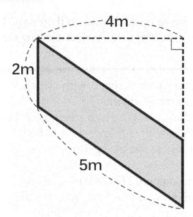

Figure 2.1.4.01 A problem commonly used in Japanese mathematics textbooks for grade 5.

This unit carefully guides students through various strategies, such as counting unit squares and equivalent-area transformation, until they discover the formula for finding the area of a parallelogram. By asking them to closely examine the difference between rectangles and parallelograms they will gain a deeper understanding of both. Working through a variety of problems on their own allows students to make mistakes which reflect their lack of understanding of key points, which will be discussed thoroughly and resolved as a class. In this way, students will be able to derive the formula for finding the area of a parallelogram on their own. This process will help them internalize the meaning and importance of base and height and prepare them to find the area formulas for other shapes they will encounter.

UNIT FLOW

Lesson	Lesson title and main learning objectives	Time
1	"Does the area of the shape change?"	60 min
	Students will watch the teacher's demonstration, displayed using dynamic geometry software such as GeoGebra, and see that a quadrilateral can easily tilt and change its shape from a rectangle to parallelogram without changing the lengths of its sides. They will then think about how to find the area of a parallelogram based on the formula for finding the area of a rectangle.	
2	"How can we calculate the area of parallelograms?"	60 min
	Students will derive the formula for finding the area of a parallelogram.	
3 and 4	"Let's use the formula to find the area of more parallelograms!"	60 min
	Students will become comfortable calculating the area of various parallelograms by identifying the necessary measurements, base and height, and using the area formula.	+ 60 min

Lesson 1: "Does the Area of the Shape Change?"

OBJECTIVES

- Students will deepen their understanding of measuring the area of a shape.
- Students will understand that quadrilaterals with the same perimeter may not necessarily have the same area.
- Students will devise a way to calculate the area of a parallelogram.

LESSON FLOW

Steps, questions from the teacher, activities, and anticipated student responses	Support from the teacher	Check understanding
1. Introduction Show Figure 2.1.4.02 and present the following task.	Encourage students to share their prior knowledge.	Is each student comfortable using the term "rectangle"?
		Does each student recall the formula for finding the area of rectangles?

> Let's calculate the area of the rectangle.

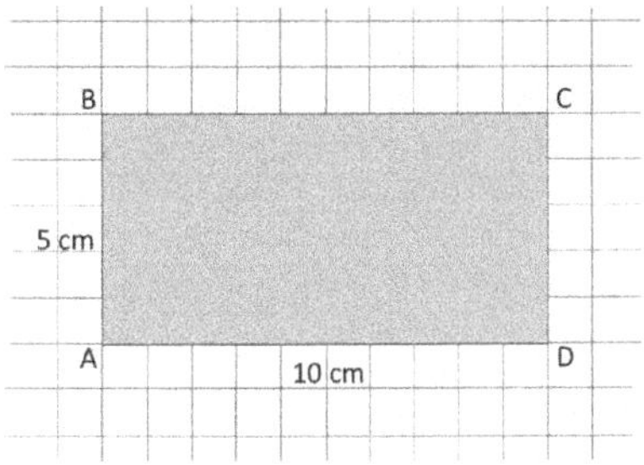

Figure 2.1.4.02

Help the class remember the area formula for rectangles.

- Since it is a rectangle, the area can be calculated using the formula length × width.
- We can count the number of small squares (unit squares).
- The area of the rectangle is 50 cm².

2. Posing the problem Help students recognize that a rectangle can easily tilt into a parallelogram without changing the lengths of its sides by giving a demonstration using dynamic geometry software, such as GeoGebra.	Provide a worksheet of the rectangle and the parallelogram shown in Figure 2.1.4.03, so students can measure the lengths and see which measurements stay the same.	Does each student understand that the sides of the rectangle and the parallelogram have the same lengths?

Steps, questions from the teacher, activities, and anticipated student responses	Support from the teacher	Check understanding

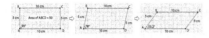

Figure 2.1.4.03

When the rectangle tilts into a parallelogram, which measurements stay the same and which change?

- The width does not change.
- The length does not change.
- The perimeter does not change.
- Each angle changes.

Let students use a ruler and protractor if they want.

Help the students realize that the area of the rectangle seems like it becomes smaller when the shape becomes more slanted.

Does each student understand that the area of the shape seems like it becomes smaller even though the lengths of the sides have not changed?

> When the shape changes from the rectangle to a parallelogram, does the area of the shape also change or does it stay the same?

Possible student responses:

a) They incorrectly assume that the area remains the same because the length and width stay the same.

b) They realize the area becomes smaller as the shape becomes more slanted.

Demonstrate using dynamic geometry software what it looks like when the shape becomes even more slanted.

Show Figure 2.1.4.04 and present the following task.

> Let's find a way to figure out the area of this parallelogram.

Give each student a worksheet with the parallelogram on a 1 cm² grid as shown in Figure 2.1.4.04.

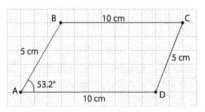

Figure 2.1.4.04

Steps, questions from the teacher, activities, and anticipated student responses	Support from the teacher	Check understanding
3. Student problem-solving/ anticipated student responses		Does each student come up with a way to find the area?
a) Counting the total number of unit squares one by one and finding that there are 40 unit squares. Therefore, the area of the parallelogram is 40 cm².		
b) Decomposing and rearranging the parallelogram into a rectangle, and using the area formula for a rectangle, length × width. 4 × 10 = 40. Therefore, the area of the parallelogram is 40 cm² (see Figure 2.1.4.05).		

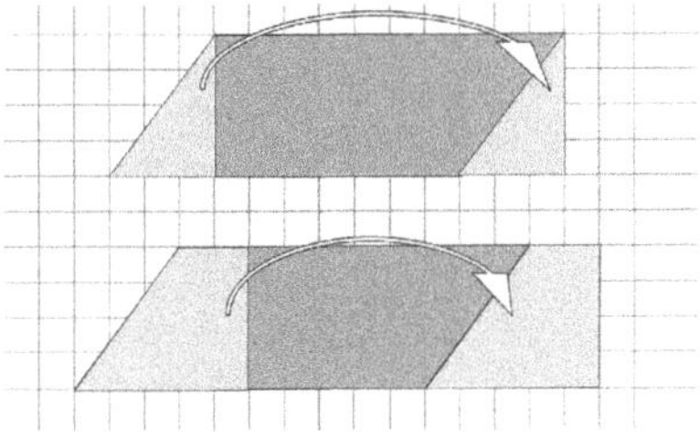

Figure 2.1.4.05

c) Mistakenly multiplying the adjacent sides.

4. Comparison and discussion	Organize the students' solutions and ideas on the board in order to help them understand the discussion.	Does each student understand that the area formula for rectangles can be used to calculate the area of the parallelogram?
Ask students to explain their solutions to the class.		
Facilitate the students' discussion about their solutions and help them realize that they can use multiplication to find the area of the parallelogram.		
Introduce the terms "base" and "height" as important measurements necessary for finding the area of a parallelogram.	Help students see that it is easier to find the area by multiplying the base by the height, rather than by trying to count unit squares.	
Help students understand why the area of parallelograms can be found by multiplying the base by the height.		

(*Continued*)

Steps, questions from the teacher, activities, and anticipated student responses	Support from the teacher	Check understanding

5. Apply the learning to another situation

Show Figure 2.1.4.06 and present the following task:

> Let's calculate the area of a more slanted parallelogram by changing it into a rectangle with the same area.

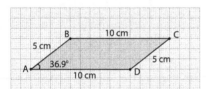

Figure 2.1.4.06

Help students recognize that even though the perimeter stays the same, the area of the shape keeps changing as it becomes more slanted.

6. Summarizing

Help each student identify the learning from the class and record it in their notes.

- Even though the perimeter stays the same, the area of a shape changes as it becomes more slanted.
- We can calculate the area of a parallelogram by applying the area formula for a rectangle. We need to measure the base and height in order to find the area of a parallelogram.

Support from the teacher column:

Give each student a worksheet with the parallelogram on a 1 cm² grid like Figure 2.1.4.06.

You may use dynamic geometry software such as GeoGebra to show students how the shape moves so they can visualize how the area changes.

Check understanding column:

Does each student understand how to change the parallelogram into a rectangle with the same area and calculate the area by applying the area formula for a rectangle?

Does every student see how the area starts changing once it becomes a parallelogram and how it continues to change as the parallelogram becomes more slanted?

Does every student write down the summary in their notes?

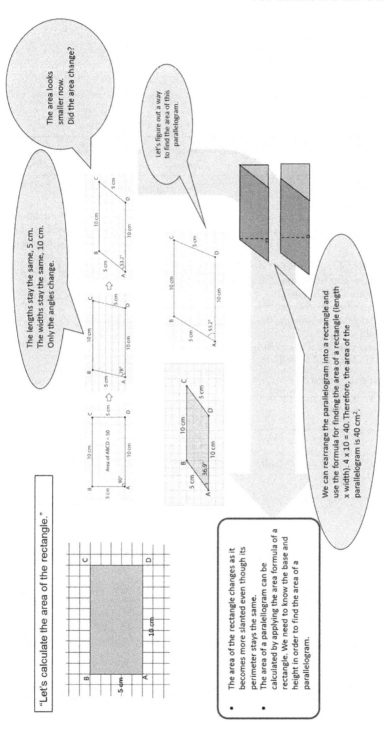

Figure 2.1.4.07 *Neriage* Map for Lesson 1: "Does the area of the shape change?"

Lesson 2: "How Can We Calculate the Area of Parallelograms?"

OBJECTIVES

● Students will derive the formula for finding the area of a parallelogram.

LESSON FLOW

Steps, questions from the teacher, activities, and anticipated student responses	Support from the teacher	Check understanding
1. Introduction Ask some students to share what they wrote in their notebook in the previous lesson to help the class recall what they learned. ● Even though the perimeter stays the same, the area of a shape changes as it becomes more slanted. ● We can calculate the area of a parallelogram by applying the area formula for a rectangle. We need to measure the base and height in order to find the area of a parallelogram.	Help students recall the previous lesson by again using dynamic geometry software to demonstrate how the area of a parallelogram changes as the shape becomes more slanted, even though the perimeter stays the same.	Does every student understand that base and height are the necessary measurements for calculating the area of a parallelogram?
2. Posing the problem Show Figure 2.1.4.08 and pose the following problem. Measure the necessary lengths and calculate the area of the parallelogram.	Have students work in pairs. Give each pair a worksheet that shows the actual size of the parallelogram (see Figure 2.1.4.13) so that students can measure the lengths using a ruler or triangle.	Does each student understand that there may be a couple of different ways to find the area?

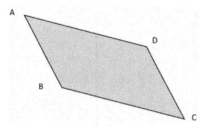

Figure 2.1.4.08

Reprinted from Fujii & Iitaka (2011, p. B32)

Steps, questions from the teacher, activities, and anticipated student responses	Support from the teacher	Check understanding
3. Student problem-solving/ anticipated student responses • Measure either side BC or side AD as the base and measure the perpendicular height. Multiply the base by the height to find the area of the parallelogram. (6 cm × 3 cm = 18 cm²) • Measure either side CD or side AB as the base and measure the perpendicular height. Multiply the base by the height to find the area of the parallelogram. (4 cm × 4.5 cm = 18 cm²) • Realize that there may be two different ways to identify the base and height. Calculate the area in two different ways using the two different sets of base and the height. (6 cm × 3 cm = 18 cm² and 4 cm × 4.5 cm = 18 cm²)	Encourage students who have already come up with one way to calculate the area to think about if there is another way to find the area by choosing a different side to be the base.	Does each student come up with at least one way to calculate the area?

4. Comparison and discussion

Using Figure 2.1.4.09 shown to the right, help students understand that there are two different ways to calculate the area of the parallelogram:

1. If we consider side BC as the base of the parallelogram, the height will be the length of the segment that is perpendicular to side BC.
2. If we consider side CD as the base of the parallelogram, the height will be the length of the segment that is perpendicular to side CD.

Help students understand that the area of a parallelogram can be calculated as base × height.

The base and height must be perpendicular to each other.

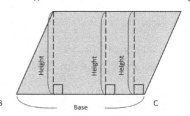

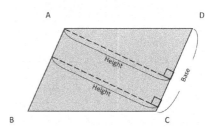

Figure 2.1.4.09

(Continued)

Steps, questions from the teacher, activities, and anticipated student responses	Support from the teacher	Check understanding
5. Summarizing Help each student identify the learning from the class and record it in their notes. • The formula for finding the area of a parallelogram is: area of parallelogram = base × height • The base and height must be perpendicular to each other. • There may be a couple of different ways to calculate the area of a parallelogram, depending on which side you consider the base.		Does every student write down the summary in their notes?

Lesson 3: "Let's Use the Formula to Find the Area of More Parallelograms! (1)"

OBJECTIVES

• Students will become comfortable calculating the area of various parallelograms by using the formula.

LESSON FLOW

Steps, questions from the teacher, activities, and anticipated student responses	Support from the teacher	Check understanding
1. Introduction Ask some students to share what they wrote in their notebook in the previous lesson to help the class recall what they learned. • We can calculate the area of a parallelogram by applying the area formula that we derived.	Help students recall the previous lesson.	Does every student recall that base and height are the necessary measurements for calculating the area of a parallelogram?

Steps, questions from the teacher, activities, and anticipated student responses	Support from the teacher	Check understanding
2. Posing the problem Show Figure 2.1.4.10 and pose the following problem: Think about how to find the area of parallelogram ABCD on the figure by applying the area formula you derived. Consider side BC as the base of the parallelogram. 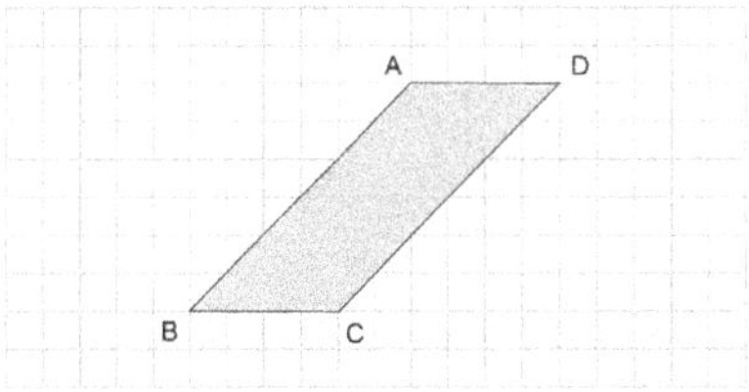	Have students work in pairs. Give each pair several copies of worksheets that show the actual size of the parallelogram so that students can cut out the shapes and rearrange them. Provide scissors and glue if the students want.	Does each student understand that there may be a couple of different ways to find the area?

Figure 2.1.4.10

3. Student problem-solving/ anticipated student responses • See the *Neriage* Map (Figure 2.1.4.11) for Lesson 3: "Let's use the formula to find the area of more parallelograms! (1)"	Encourage students who have already come up with one way to calculate the area, to think about the height corresponding to the given base.	Does each student come up with at least one way to calculate the area?
4. Comparison and discussion • Through the discussion, help students understand a variety of ways to apply the area formula to find the parallelogram area. • Discuss how to find out the height corresponding to the given base.	Provide the students who want to show how they cut and rearranged the parallelogram with scissors and worksheets.	Does each student understand their classmates' ideas to calculate the area?
5. Summarizing Help each student identify the learning from the class and record it in their notes. • You can consider the height of a parallelogram as the distance between the lines obtained by extending the base and its opposite side. This makes it easier to calculate the area formula.		Does every student write down the summary in their notes?

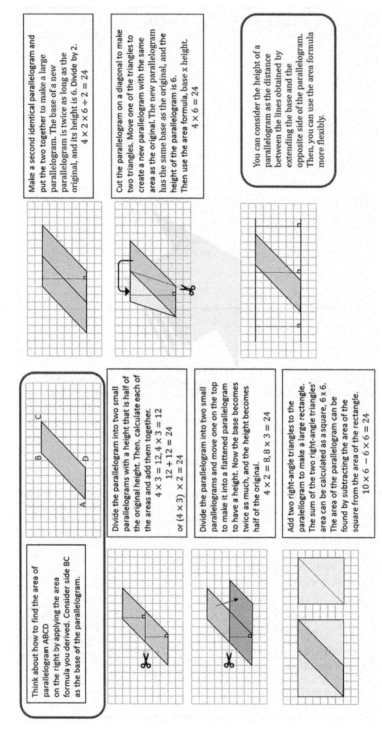

Think about how to find the area of parallelogram ABCD on the right by applying the area formula you derived. Consider side BC as the base of the parallelogram.

Make a second identical parallelogram and put the two together to make a large parallelogram. The base of a new parallelogram is twice as long as the original, and its height is 6. Divide by 2.

$4 \times 2 \times 6 \div 2 = 24$

Cut the parallelogram on a diagonal to make two triangles. Move one of the triangles to create a new parallelogram with the same area as the original. The new parallelogram has the same base as the original, and the height of the parallelogram is 6.
Then use the area formula, base × height.

$4 \times 6 = 24$

You can consider the height of a parallelogram as the distance between the lines obtained by extending the base and the opposite side of the parallelogram. Then, you can use the area formula more flexibly.

Divide the parallelogram into two small parallelograms with a height that is half of the original height. Then, calculate each of the areas and add them together.

$4 \times 3 = 12, 4 \times 3 = 12$
$12 + 12 = 24$
or $(4 \times 3) \times 2 = 24$

Divide the parallelogram into two small parallelograms and move one on the top to make it into a flattened parallelogram to have a height. Now the base becomes twice as much, and the height becomes half of the original.

$4 \times 2 = 8, 8 \times 3 = 24$

Add two right-angle triangles to the parallelogram to make a large rectangle. The sum of the two right-angle triangles' area can be calculated as a square, 6 × 6. The area of the parallelogram can be found by subtracting the area of the square from the area of the rectangle.

$10 \times 6 - 6 \times 6 = 24$

Figure 2.1.4.11 *Neriage* Map for Lesson 3: "Let's use the formula to find the area of more parallelograms! (1)"

Lesson 4: "Let's Use the Formula to Find the Area of More Parallelograms! (2)"

OBJECTIVES

• Students will become comfortable calculating the area of various parallelograms by identifying the base and height and using the area formula.

INSTRUCTION

• This is an exercise lesson. Students will deepen their understanding of the necessary measurements for finding the area of parallelograms by finding the areas of parallelograms, such as:

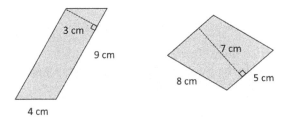

Figure 2.1.4.12

Figure 2.1.4.13 is the actual size of the parallelogram discussed in Lesson 2. You may use this figure to create worksheets so that students can use a ruler or triangle to measure the base and height to calculate the area.

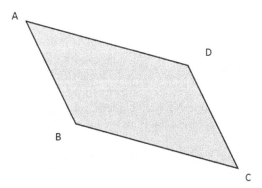

Figure 2.1.4.13

Reprinted from Fujii & Iitaka, (2011) Atarashii Sansuu Grade 5 p. B32, Tokyo Shoseki, Tokyo, Japan

2.1.5 TTP Unit: *"Introducing Fractions"*

Grade: Lower elementary

In this unit, students will learn that a fraction is a number that represents part of a larger, equally partitioned whole. In each lesson, they will be introduced to this concept through everyday situations and will use tape strips as manipulatives in order to become comfortable working with fractions in a concrete way. In the first of the three lessons, students will have to figure out how to represent one portion of an object divided into equal parts in order to complete measurement tasks. In the second lesson, they will experience how fractions can also represent a collection of unit fractions and learn about fractional notation. Finally, in the third lesson, students will create and name fractions of various sizes and practice putting them on a number line. In this way, students will come to see fractions as numbers.

PRIOR LEARNING REQUIRED

- CCSS.Math.Content.1.NBT.A.1 "Count to 120, starting at any number less than 120. In this range, read and write numerals and represent a number of objects with a written numeral."
- CCSS.Math.Content.2.MD.B.6 "Represent whole numbers as lengths from 0 on a number line diagram with equally spaced points corresponding to the numbers 0, 1, 2, . . ., and represent whole-number sums and differences within 100 on a number line diagram."
- CCSS.Math.Content.2.G.A.3 "Partition circles and rectangles into two, three, or four equal shares, describe the shares using the words halves, thirds, half of, a third of, etc., and describe the whole as two halves, three thirds, four fourths. Recognize that equal shares of identical wholes need not have the same shape."

MAIN CCSS ADDRESSED IN THIS UNIT

- CCSS.Math.Content.3.NF.A.1 "Understand a fraction $1/b$ as the quantity formed by 1 part when a whole is partitioned into b equal parts; understand a fraction a/b as the quantity formed by a parts of size $1/b$."
- CCSS.Math.Content.3.NF.A.2 "Understand a fraction as a number on the number line; represent fractions on a number line diagram."

RELATED LATER LEARNING

- CCSS.Math.Content.3.NF.A.3 "Explain equivalence of fractions in special cases, and compare fractions by reasoning about their size."
- CCSS.Math.Content.4.NF.introduction "Number and Operations—Fractions: Extend understanding of fraction equivalence and ordering. Build fractions from unit fractions by applying and extending previous

understandings of operations on whole numbers. Understand decimal notation for fractions, and compare decimal fractions."

Fractions are an essential elementary grade topic. At the same time, they are one of the most challenging topics for students to understand (National Mathematics Advisory Panel, 2008). Many students have seen fractions in everyday life, such as half-miles on road signs and quarter-pounds on fast-food menus. However, they may still not recognize fractions as numbers and therefore struggle to use them comfortably. Gunderson and Gunderson (1957) argue that the concept of fractions can be successfully introduced as early as second grade using manipulatives. However, they also say that in order for second grade students to truly see fractions as numbers, they need to be introduced to the concept gradually, starting with the concrete and then transitioning to the semi-concrete before finally dealing with them in the abstract (Gunderson & Gunderson, 1957).

Both modern curricula and academic research reflect the idea that students can be introduced to fractions in the lower elementary levels. The national curriculum for elementary mathematics in Japan states that fractions should be introduced in second grade, by giving students concrete tasks to help students understand that fractions represent parts of an equally divided object (Ministry of Education Culture Sports Science and Technology Japan, 2017). Thompson and Saldanha posit that fractions should be introduced starting with unit fractions (2003). Once students are comfortable working with unit fractions, they are then ready to learn that $\frac{2}{3}$ represents a collection of two $\frac{1}{3}$ units (Thompson & Saldanha, 2003). To help students understand the concept of units better, Gunderson and Gunderson write that students who work well with fractions use words instead of fractional notation when first learning about fractions (1957). For example, they would write "2 thirds" instead of $\frac{2}{3}$ (1957). In this way, students can see that the "third" of "1 third" is a unit of measurement.

It is crucial for students to understand that fractions represent sizes of quantities just like whole numbers, so that they will be prepared to learn how to use fractions to represent proportions in the later grades. The national curriculum in Singapore emphasizes that the concept that fractions are part of a whole can be introduced in the second grade, but the concept that fractions can be used to represent proportions should not be introduced until the fourth grade (Ministry of Education Singapore, 2006). The Japanese national curriculum states that even though some of the basic ideas of fractions should be introduced in the second grade, using fractions to represent proportions should not be introduced until the fifth grade (Ministry of Education Culture Sports Science and Technology Japan, 2017). This reflects the importance of introducing fractions properly so that students will be prepared to learn how to compare them and work with proportions later on.

This lesson unit, "Introducing fractions," consists of three lessons based on the above discussion of how best to introduce fractions. The design of this unit is largely based on a third grade level textbook from the most widely used public school mathematics textbook series in Japan, *Atarashii Sansuu*

(Hironaka & Sugiyama, 2000), which was translated into English and published as *Mathematics for Elementary School 3B* (Hironaka & Sugiyama, 2006). The following key points from this textbook have been incorporated into this unit:

- Fractions are introduced as being part of whole; they express an amount obtained as a result of equal partitioning.
- Fractions are used to express quantities of less than 1 in measurement contexts.
- Diagrams, such as tape diagrams and area diagrams, are used to help students understand that a fraction can be considered as a collection of unit fractions.
- Tape diagrams and number lines are used to help students see that fractions are numbers just like whole numbers.

The tape diagrams are made of actual tape strips, and tape strips will also be given to students to work with fractions in a concrete setting. Furthermore, since this textbook was originally written in Japanese for children who live in Japan, the following key ideas have also been added to maximize the benefits of learning for English speaking children who live outside Japan:

- Examples of fractions from students' everyday lives will be shown to help them see how commonly fractions are used.
- Students will be encouraged to write fractions using words before learning fractional notation. For example, writing "2 thirds," so that they can see "thirds" as a unit.

In this way, students will become comfortable working with fractions the same way they do whole numbers.

UNIT FLOW

Lesson	Lesson title and main learning objectives	Time
1	"How can we express fractional parts?" Students will realize that fractions can be seen in their everyday lives. They will understand that fractions are used to express an amount obtained as a result of equal partitioning and can be used to express quantities less than 1 (unit fractions).	60 min
2	"How can we express fractions?" Students will understand that a fraction can be considered as a collection of unit fractions. They will learn fractional notation.	60 min
3	"Fraction sizes" Students will become comfortable making their own non-unit fractions from a collection of unit fractions. Students will realize that fractions can be put on a number line.	60 min

Lesson 1: "How Can We Express Fractional Parts?"

OBJECTIVES

- Students will realize that fractions can be seen in their everyday lives.
- Students will understand that fractions are used to express an amount obtained as a result of equal partitioning and are used to express quantities less than 1 (unit fractions).

LESSON FLOW

Steps, questions from the teacher, activities, and anticipated student responses	Support from the teacher	Check understanding
1. Introduction Show the images of road signs displaying fractions (Figure 2.1.5.01) and ask the following question: What does each number on the road sign represent?	If some of the students seem unfamiliar with the term fraction, avoid using it until the class informally defines the term. Encourage students to share their prior knowledge.	Is each student comfortable using the term "fraction"? Does each student understand what the fractions on the road signs represent?

Figure 2.1.5.01

Lead a class discussion on what the fractions on the road signs represent using the students' prior knowledge regarding whole numbers, measurements of distance, and fractions. Ask students what they know about fractions and where else they have seen them.

(Continued)

Steps, questions from the teacher, activities, and anticipated student responses	Support from the teacher	Check understanding
2. Posing the problem Show an actual 1⅓ meter tape strip divided into 1 meter and an unlabeled fractional part as in Figure 2.1.5.02 and present the following task: Look at this tape strip. I made this tape strip by measuring the length around one of the trees outside. It's a bit longer than 1 meter. So there is the 1 meter part and this other part. What can we call the length of this other part? You can use the 1 meter tape strip to compare lengths.	Have students work in pairs. Each pair will use a 1 meter tape strip and a ⅓ meter tape strip. Encourage students to use 1 meter as a reference to express the length of the fractional part.	Does each student understand that the fractional part can be expressed using 1 meter as a reference?

1 m	☐m

Figure 2.1.5.02

Provide the set of tapes (actual length) shown in Figure 2.1.5.03 to students to help them solve the problem.

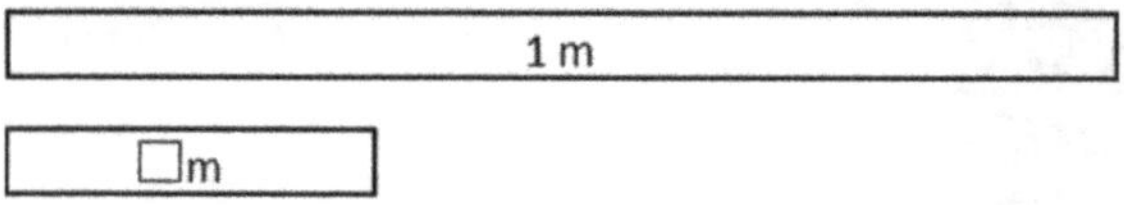

1 m

☐m

Figure 2.1.5.03

| **3. Student problem-solving/ anticipated student responses**

• It's about half of 1 meter.
• It's about a quarter of 1 meter.
• It's as long as what you get when you divide 1 meter into three equal parts.
• It's a third of one meter.
• Some students might use other units of measurement, such as the length of their hand or notebook. Others may use yards or feet. | Have each student write their way of expressing the fractional part in their notes. | Does each student come up with a way to represent the fractional part? |

Steps, questions from the teacher, activities, and anticipated student responses	Support from the teacher	Check understanding
4. Comparison and discussion Compare and discuss each approach that students used to express the fractional part of the tape strip, so that they understand each other's ways of thinking. Help students understand that a fraction can be used to express the length of a fractional part of the tape strip. Help students see that the length of the fractional part is "a third of 1 meter" because the 1 meter tape strip is three times as long as the fractional part.	Help students see that using a formal unit, such as 1 meter, as a reference is very helpful when expressing quantities. Have students write the length of the fractional part using words for the unit, "a third of 1 meter."	Does each student understand that the fractional part can be expressed using "third of 1 meter" as a unit?
5. Apply the learning to a similar situation 1. Show students actual tape strips as in the image (Figure 2.1.5.04) and ask them the following:	Have students work in pairs. Give each student 1 meter tape strips for each problem so that they can make their own half, fifth, and quarter of 1 meter tape strips.	Does each student understand how to express the length and write it in words?

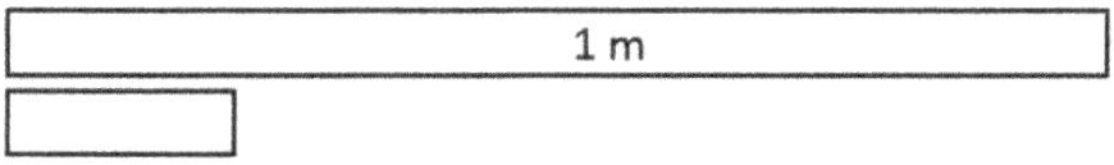

I'm going to show you some tape strips. One is 1 meter and the other is shorter than 1 meter. Using what we just learned, what can we call the length of the shorter one?

1 m

Figure 2.1.5.04

Once they find the length of the shorter tape strip (a fifth of 1 meter), have them write down the length using words.

(Continued)

Steps, questions from the teacher, activities, and anticipated student responses	*Support from the teacher*	*Check understanding*
2. Show students actual tape strips as in the image (Figure 2.1.5.05) and ask them the following:	Help students recognize that a fourth of 1 meter is called a "quarter of a meter."	Does each student make a half, fifth, and quarter of 1 meter length tape strips?

> Find the length of the shorter tape strip.

1 m

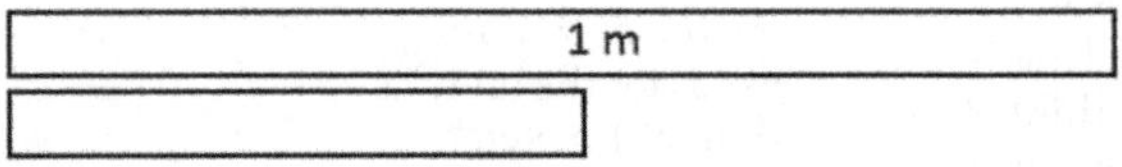

Figure 2.1.5.05

Once they find the length of
the shorter tape strip (a half of
1 meter), have them write down the
length using words, "a half of
1 meter."

3. Ask the following:

> Let's make a fourth of a
> 1 meter tape strip from a
> 1 meter tape strip.

Ask a couple of students to explain how
they made their fourth of
1 meter tape strips.

Ask the other students to verify if those
tape strips are a fourth of
1 meter long.

6. Summarizing

Help each student identify the learning
from the class and record it in their
notes.

- The length of fractions shorter than
  1 meter can be shown using words,
  such as a third
  of 1 meter, a half of 1 meter, a
  quarter (fourth) of 1 meter, and a
  fifth of 1 meter.

Does every
student write
down the
summary in
their notes?

Lesson 2: "How Can We Express Fractions?"

OBJECTIVES

- Students will understand that a fraction can be considered as a collection of unit fractions.
- Students will learn fractional notation.

LESSON FLOW

Steps, questions from the teacher, activities, and anticipated student responses	Support from the teacher	Check understanding
1. Introduction Ask some students to share what they wrote in their notebook in the previous lesson to help the class recall what they learned. • The length of fractions shorter than 1 meter can be shown using words, such as a third of 1 meter, a half of 1 meter, a quarter (fourth) of 1 meter, and a fifth of 1 meter.	Put the tape strips used during the previous lesson on the board to help students recall what they called each length of tape strip.	Can every student identify the length of each tape strip?
2. Posing the problem Show two tape strips, one 1 meter and the other $\frac{2}{3}$ of a meter, as in the image (Figure 2.1.5.06) and ask the following: The length of this tape strip is shorter than 1 meter. Think about what we learned yesterday. What can we call the length of this tape strip? You can use the 1 meter strip to compare lengths. 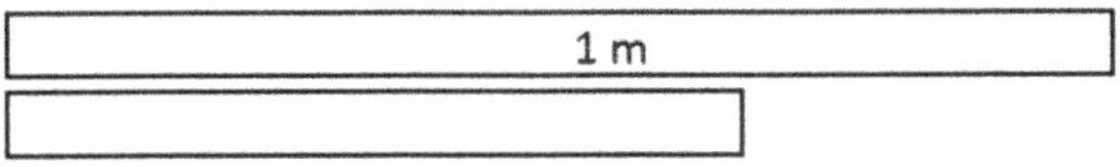	Have students work in pairs. Give each pair a 1 meter tape strip and a $\frac{2}{3}$ meter tape strip to use. Encourage students to use the tape strips from the previous lesson as a reference.	Does each student understand that the fraction can be expressed using 1 meter as a reference?

Figure 2.1.5.06

(Continued)

Steps, questions from the teacher, activities, and anticipated student responses	*Support from the teacher*	*Check understanding*
3. Student problem-solving/ anticipated student responses • It's a bit longer than a half of 1 meter. • It's twice as long as a third of 1 meter. • It's two of the thirds of 1 meter. • It's 2 thirds of 1 meter.	Have each student write their way of figuring out the length of the $\frac{2}{3}$ meter tape strip in their notes.	Does each student come up with a way to represent the $\frac{2}{3}$ meter tape strip?
4. Comparison and discussion Help students understand that the length of the fraction is twice as long as the third of a meter tape strip.	Have students write the length of the fraction using words for the unit, "2 thirds of 1 meter."	Does each student understand that the fraction can be expressed using "thirds of 1 meter" as a unit?
Help students understand that the fraction can be expressed as a collection of the thirds.		
Help students understand the fraction can be expressed using the words, "2 thirds of 1 meter."		
Introduce fractional notation to replace the use of words to express fractional parts.		

> The length 2 thirds of 1 meter is written as $\frac{2}{3}$ m and is read as "two thirds meter."

Steps, questions from the teacher, activities, and anticipated student responses	Support from the teacher	Check understanding
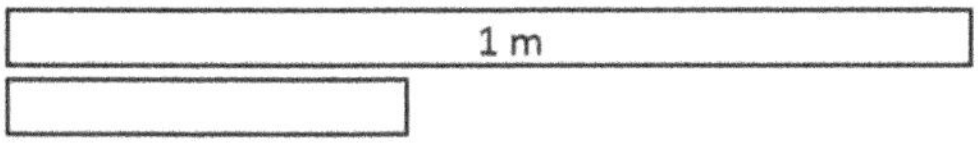 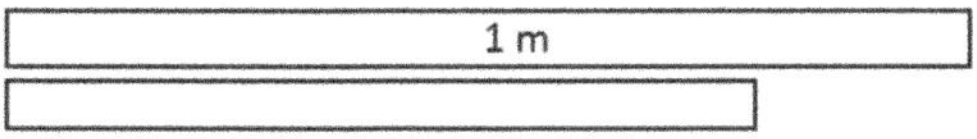 **5. Apply the learning to another situation** 1. Show two tape strips, one 1 meter and the other $\frac{2}{5}$ of a meter, as in the image (Figure 2.1.5.07) and ask the following: How can we find the length of the shorter tape strip using what we just learned?	Have students work in pairs. Give each pair tape strips for each problem. Once students find the length of each tape strip, have them write down the amount using a fraction.	Does every student understand how to express the length of each tape strip using a fraction?

```
|              1 m              |
| |
```

Figure 2.1.5.07

2. Show two tape strips, one 1 meter and the other $\frac{3}{4}$ of a meter, as in the image (Figure 2.1.5.08) and ask the following:

Find the length of the shorter tape strip.

```
|              1 m              |
|        |
```

Figure 2.1.5.08

6. Summarizing Let students practice using fractional notation to represent the fractions that they expressed in words during the lesson activities. Help each student identify the learning from the class and record it in their notes. • 3 fourths of 1 meter can be written as $\frac{3}{4}$ meter. • Numbers like $\frac{3}{4}$ are called fractions. • The 4 is the denominator. It tell us the unit, fourths. • The 3 is the numerator. It tells us how many of the units there are.		Is every student able to express the fractions using fractional notation? Does every student write down the summary in their notes?

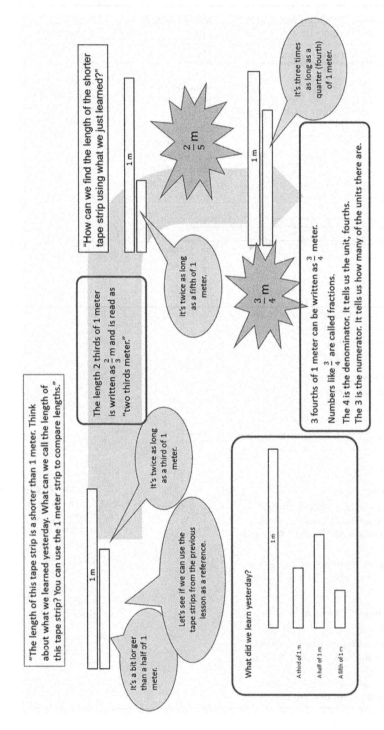

Figure 2.1.5.09 Neriage Map for Lesson 2: "How can we express fractions?"

Lesson 3: "Fraction Sizes"

OBJECTIVES

- Students will become comfortable making their own non-unit fractions from a collection of unit fractions.
- Students will learn that fractions can be put on number lines.

LESSON FLOW

Steps, questions from the teacher, activities, and anticipated student responses	Support from the teacher	Check understanding
1. Introduction Ask some students to share what they wrote in their notebook in the previous lesson to help the class recall what they learned.		
2. Posing the problem Present students with the following task:	Have students work in pairs. Each pair will use all the tape strips from the previous lessons (such as $\frac{1}{3}$ meter, $\frac{1}{4}$ meter, $\frac{3}{4}$ meter, etc.) to enjoy making several different lengths of tape strip by combining tape strips that are the same unit together. Each group will have a paper roll to use to make their own tape strips.	Does each student understand that the fractions can be expressed using 1 meter as a reference? Does each student understand that they can only put together tape strips that are the same unit?

> Let's create many different lengths of tape strips using the tape strips that we've been using up until now.

Ask students to put tape strips of the same unit fractions together, using a variety of different unit fractions:

- Half (meter)
- Third (meter)
- Quarter/fourth (meter)
- Fifth (meter)

Remind students that they can only put together tape strips that are the same unit. ($\frac{1}{3}$ meter and $\frac{1}{3}$ meter can be put together to make $\frac{2}{3}$ of 1 meter, but $\frac{1}{3}$ meter and $\frac{1}{4}$ meter cannot)

(Continued)

Steps, questions from the teacher, activities, and anticipated student responses	Support from the teacher	Check understanding
3. Student problem-solving/ anticipated student responses • 2 halves of 1 meter • 2 thirds of 1 meter, 3 thirds of 1 meter • 2 fourths of 1 meter, 3 fourths of 1 meter, 4 fourths of 1 meter, 2 quarters of 1 meter, 3 quarters of 1 meter, 4 quarters of 1 meter • 2 fifths of 1 meter, 3 fifths of 1 meter, 4 fifths of 1 meters, 5 fifths of 1 meter • $\frac{2}{2}, \frac{2}{3}, \frac{3}{3}, \frac{2}{4}, \frac{3}{4}, \frac{4}{4}, \frac{2}{5}, \frac{3}{5}, \frac{4}{5}, \frac{5}{5}$ • Adding lengths of different unit fractions together.	Have each student record the fractions they made in their notes.	Does each student create new fractions from collections of unit fractions?
4. Comparison and discussion Through sharing their fractions, students will have opportunities to express, interpret, and validate their own and each other's fractions using both words and fractional notation. Help students understand that the fractions they have created were made by combining fractions of the same unit. Organize fractions according to the size of the unit fraction. Put fractions with the same denominator on the same number line. Refer to the example of board organization shown in Figure 2.1.5.10. Compare the size of fractions with the same denominators.	Encourage students to write the length of the fractions using both words, such as "2 thirds of 1 meter," and fractional notation.	Does each student understand that the fractions can be expressed in both words and fractional notation?
5. Summarizing Help each student identify the learning from the class and record it in their notes. • Fractions can be put on a number line just like whole numbers.		Does every student write down the summary in their notes?

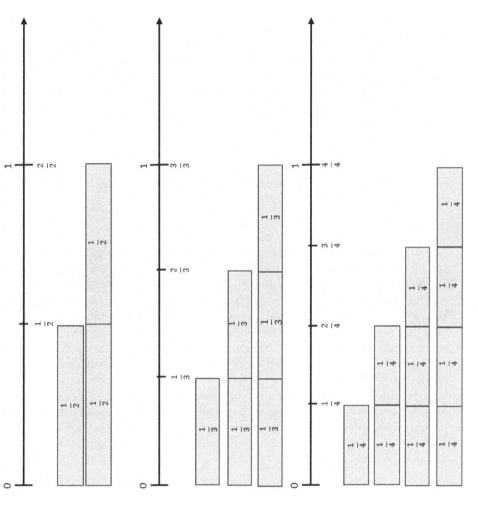

Figure 2.1.5.10 Example of how to organize diagrams on the board.

2.2 TTP Lessons to Expand Understanding

Examples of the TTP lessons in this section require students to expand their understanding of mathematical practices outlined by the Common Core State Standards (2010). Unlike the previous examples shown in section 2.1, these can be stand-alone lessons to challenge students' mathematical thinking and ability to solve problems. I call these lessons "Spotlight Lessons," to highlight that you can add them to your existing curriculum. Please refer to the prior learning required, main objective, and related future learning outlined for each lesson in terms of the CCSS, to determine if and when a lesson would be appropriate for your students.

2.2.1 Spotlight Lesson: "Curious Subtraction"

Grade: Lower elementary level or lower secondary level

MAIN OBJECTIVE

This TTP lesson is designed to extend students' understanding of place value and subtraction with two-digit numbers. Students will apply their understanding of subtraction using place value to find interesting patterns among specific sets of subtractions. They will see what happens when we take two-digit numbers in which the tens place is two units more than the ones place and subtract from that another two-digit number which has the units in the place values reversed, such as 53 and 35. The difference will always be 18. This will make them curious about the pattern and they can continue to investigate various calculations. Through this process, lower elementary students will have to perform various subtractions with two-digit numbers, helping them develop fluency in calculating subtraction with two-digit numbers and expand their understanding of base ten place value notation. Lower secondary level students can also apply algebra to further examine these patterns and uncover the underlying reason.

PRIOR LEARNING REQUIRED

- CCSS.Math.Content.1.NBT.B.2 "Understand that the two digits of a two-digit number represent amounts of tens and ones."
- CCSS.Math.Content.1.NBT.C.4 "Add within 100, including adding a two-digit number and a one-digit number, and adding a two-digit number and a multiple of 10, using concrete models or drawings and strategies based on place value, properties of operations, and/or the relationship between addition and subtraction; relate the strategy to a written method and explain the reasoning used. Understand that in adding two-digit

numbers, one adds tens and tens, ones and ones; and sometimes it is necessary to compose a ten."

MAIN CCSS ADDRESSED AND EXPANDED UPON IN THIS LESSON

- CCSS.Math.Content.1.NBT.B.2 "Understand that the two digits of a two-digit number represent amounts of tens and ones."

RELATED LATER LEARNING

- CCSS.Math.Content.2.NBT.B.5 "Fluently add and subtract within 100 using strategies based on place value, properties of operations, and/or the relationship between addition and subtraction."

LESSON FLOW

1. Begin the lesson by putting nine different number cards from 1 to 9 up on the board.

Figure 2.2.1.01

2. Ask a volunteer to pick a card.

3. The teacher will choose the second card. For example, if the volunteer selected 3, choose another card that is two unit values different, such as 5. However, the students don't know that you are intentionally doing this yet, they must discover that for themselves later.

4. Use the two cards to make two different two-digit numbers, in this case 53 and 35.

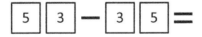

Figure 2.2.1.02

5. The class subtracts the smaller number from the larger number, 53–35, and finds that the difference is 18.

6. Ask another volunteer to pick another card and repeat the above process. If the student chooses 7, choose a number two units different, such as 9.

7. The class calculates another subtraction, in this case, 97–79, and finds that the difference is again 18.

8. Repeat this process a few times and then ask:

Is this result a coincidence or am I intentionally choosing certain numbers?

Students will realize that the teacher is always choosing a number two units apart from the first number. Furthermore, they will realize that the difference between the smaller two-digit number subtracted from the higher two-digit number made from this pair will always be 18.

9. Ask students to explore the pattern that results from number pairings that are one unit apart, such as 32–23 and 43–34.

10. Ask students to explore various patterns, such as number pairings that are 3 units apart. Please refer to the *Neriage* Map, Figure 2.2.1.03, for more examples.

11. This lesson requires a lot of writing space on the board for effective *Neriage*. The *Neriage* Map for this lesson shows how you can ask many students to share their calculations so the class can discuss the patterns. Organize their work by grouping calculations which have the same remainder together in order to help students see the patterns. This also shows them the importance of organizing their work.

12. If students are familiar with multiplication facts, they can identify that all the remainders are multiples of nine. If the two initial numbers are only one unit apart, the difference will be 9. If the two initial numbers are two units apart, such as $\boxed{3}$ and $\boxed{5}$, the difference will be 18. When the two numbers are three units apart, such as $\boxed{6}$ and $\boxed{9}$, the difference will be 27 (please refer to the *Neriage* Map for other examples).

Algebra for secondary level students
Secondary level students can use algebra to investigate the reason behind this pattern. First, let students work on their own, then facilitate a whole class discussion to share and discuss their ideas in order to uncover this mechanism using a series of equations.

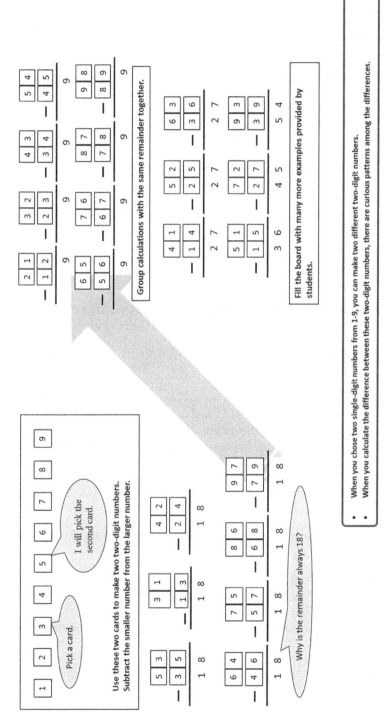

Figure 2.2.1.03 Neriage Map for "Curious subtraction"

13. Using letters a and b ($a > b$) to represent the initial single-digit numbers that the student and teacher pick, the two-digit numbers that can be made with these are:

$10a + b$, and $10b + a$

14. Students may come up with the following equation to show (the larger number) – (the smaller number):

$$10a + b - (10b + a) = 10a + b - 10b - a$$
$$= 10a - a + b - 10b$$
$$= 9a - 9b$$
$$= 9(a - b)$$

This shows that the difference between the two-digit numbers will always be a multiple of 9, and the difference between the two initial single-digit numbers determines which multiple of 9 it will be.

2.2.2 Spotlight Lesson: "Comparing Areas Using Pattern Blocks"

Grade: Lower elementary level

MAIN OBJECTIVE

This TTP lesson is based on a lesson from a Japanese teacher's guide (Takahashi & Yanase, 1997, pp. 113–122) and is designed to extend students' understanding about how to compare different areas. It builds upon students' previous experience with comparing lengths, when they learned that it is crucial to identify a common unit in order to compare lengths easily. In this lesson, students must decide how to choose a common unit to compare the size of two different shapes. The hands-on investigation helps build a solid foundation for learning how to measure area using standard units.

PRIOR LEARNING REQUIRED

- CCSS.Math.Content.K.MD.A.2 "Directly compare two objects with a measurable attribute in common, to see which object has "more of"/"less of" the attribute, and describe the difference."
- CCSS.Math.Content.K.G.B.6 "Compose simple shapes to form larger shapes."

- CCSS.Math.Content.2.OA.A.1 "Use addition and subtraction within 100 to solve one- and two-step word problems involving situations of adding to, taking from, putting together, taking apart, and comparing, with unknowns in all positions."
- CCSS.Math.Content.3.OA.A.3 "Use multiplication and division within 100 to solve word problems in situations involving equal groups, arrays, and measurement quantities."
- Students should be familiar with Pattern Blocks, a set of manipulatives consisting of six different shapes, and know the relationships among the shapes. For example, students should be able to make the shape of a yellow block using other blocks.

MAIN CCSS INTRODUCED IN THIS LESSON

- CCSS.Math.Content.3.MD.C.5 "Recognize area as an attribute of plane figures and understand concepts of area measurement."

RELATED LATER LEARNING

- CCSS.Math.Content.3.MD.C.6 "Measure areas by counting unit squares (square cm, square m, square in, square ft, and improvised units)."
- CCSS.Math.Content.3.MD.C.7 "Understand concepts of area and relate area to multiplication and addition."

LESSON FLOW

1. First, the students will work with partners to fill shapes A and B using different amounts of different pattern blocks for each.

Fill shapes A and B using the given numbers of pattern blocks without any overlaps or gaps.

Use Shape A and Shape B of Figure 2.2.2.01 to create large worksheets students can use with actual pattern blocks. The following figure shows how to lay out the Appendices side by side to create the worksheet:

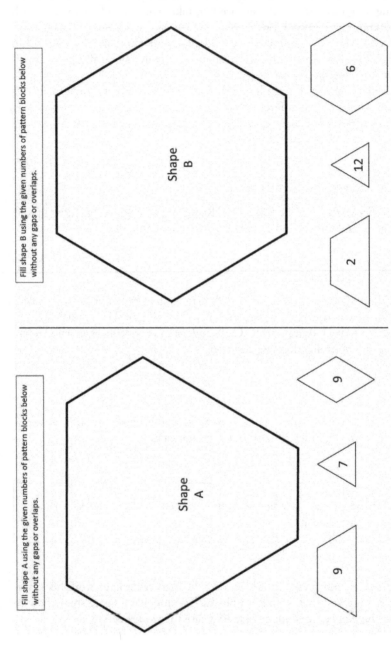

Fill shape A using the given numbers of pattern blocks below without any gaps or overlaps.

Fill shape B using the given numbers of pattern blocks below without any gaps or overlaps.

Shape A

Shape B

Note: When making copies make sure to enlarge the images so that students can use pattern blocks.

Figure 2.2.2.01

2. After students finish this task, ask them to compare the sizes of the spaces inside the shapes:

Which has a larger space inside, shape A or shape B?

---

3. Since students filled A and B with different amounts of different kinds of pattern blocks, they cannot compare the sizes by counting the numbers of the pattern blocks they used for each shape. They will have to discover that they can compare these spaces by converting some types of pattern blocks to another kind of pattern block. For example, students may realize that they can make a yellow block using three blue blocks (see Figure 2.2.2.02).

Figure 2.2.2.02

4. Students may also try to fill both A and B with the same kinds of blocks. For example, they might fill A with 3 yellow blocks, 9 red blocks, and 7 green blocks, and fill B with 6 yellow blocks, 2 red blocks, and 12 green blocks. However, even though they are using the same three kinds of blocks in each shape, it is still not easy to find out which one has more space inside.

5. They must make further conversions to compare the space of the shapes. The following are examples of the approaches students may use:

(a) Using yellow blocks to compare the space of both shapes.

Shape A: 8 yellow blocks, 1 red block, and 1 green block.
Shape B: 9 yellow blocks.

Shape B has more space inside.

(b) Using green blocks to compare the space of both shapes.

Shape A: 52 green blocks.
Shape B: 54 green blocks.

Shape B has more space inside.

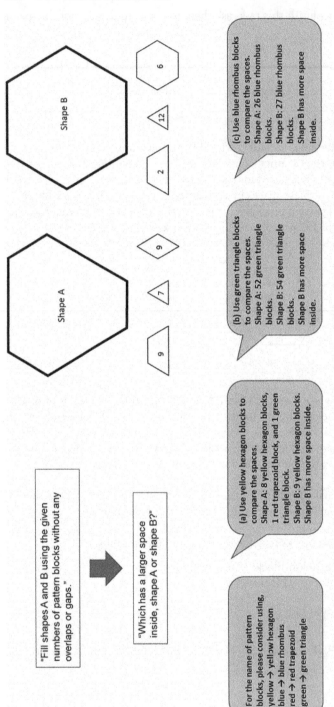

Figure 2.2.2.03 Neriage Map for "Comparing areas using pattern blocks"

Appendix Shape A

Note: When making copies make sure to enlarge the image so that students can use pattern blocks.

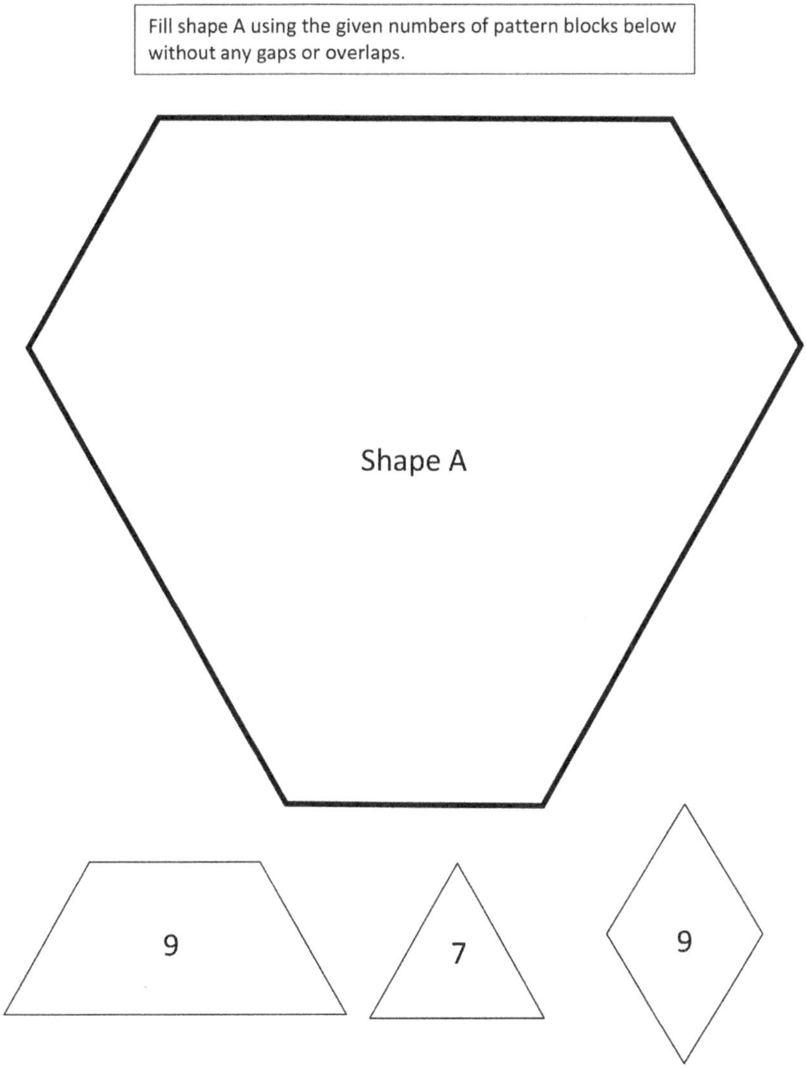

Fill shape A using the given numbers of pattern blocks below without any gaps or overlaps.

Shape A

9

7

9

Figure 2.2.2.04

Appendix Shape B

Note: When making copies make sure to enlarge the image so that students can use pattern blocks.

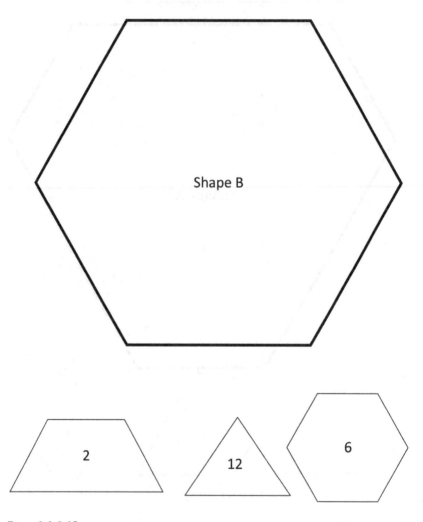

> Fill shape B using the given numbers of pattern blocks below without any gaps or overlaps.

Shape B

2   12   6

Figure 2.2.2.05

(c) Using blue blocks to compare the space of both shapes.

Shape A: 26 blue blocks.
Shape B: 27 blue blocks.

Shape B has more space inside.

6. For this lesson, the primary purpose of *Neriage* is for the students to understand the importance of using a common unit to compare two quantities. Therefore, instead of highlighting the differences among students' approaches, encourage them to see this shared idea. The *Neriage* Map (Figure 2.2.2.03) illustrates how you can organize the board to help students understand this key concept: if you use one kind of block as a common unit, you can easily compare the size of the spaces by looking at how many unit blocks there are in each space.

2.2.3 Spotlight Lesson: "Let's Make a Calendar"

Grade: Upper elementary level

MAIN OBJECTIVE

This TTP lesson deepens students' understanding of place value. It consists of a series of questions which guide students to solve a challenging problem: how can they design two cubes that both have a single-digit number on each face in order to make a calendar that can display each day of the month from 1 to 31? This interesting problem lets students explore the properties of place value and also relates to their everyday lives.

PRIOR LEARNING REQUIRED

- CCSS.Math.Content.1.NBT.B.2 "Understand that the two digits of a two-digit number represent amounts of tens and ones."
- CCSS.Math.Content.2.G.A.1 "Recognize and draw shapes having specified attributes, such as a given number of angles or a given number of equal faces. Identify triangles, quadrilaterals, pentagons, hexagons, and cubes."

MAIN CCSS ADDRESSED AND EXPANDED UPON IN THIS LESSON

- CCSS.Math.Content.1.NBT.B.2 "Understand that the two digits of a two-digit number represent amounts of tens and ones."

RELATED LATER LEARNING

- CCSS.Math.Content.3.NBT "Use place value understanding and properties of operations to perform multi-digit arithmetic."

LESSON FLOW

1. Begin the lesson by asking the following question:

> Let's make a calendar. If you can write one number on each card, how many cards do you need to display each day of the month?

Students may answer by saying we would need thirty-one cards, because the longest months have thirty-one days.

2. Encourage students to think about if they can reduce the number of cards they actually need:

> What is the fewest number of cards you need to create 1–31?

You can help students by showing them how to use two single-digit numbers to make two different two-digit numbers. This will help them realize that they don't need thirty-one individual number cards. Students may come up with the following approaches:

> We need two sets of 0–9, making for a total of twenty cards.

Figure 2.2.3.01

1. We only need one set of 0–9 and an additional set of 1–3 because we only need 1, 2, and 3 for the tens place, making for a total of thirteen cards.

Figure 2.2.3.02

2. We only need one set of 0–9 and an additional set of 1–2. We do not need two 3 cards because we do not need to make 33, making for a total of twelve cards.

Figure 2.2.3.03

3. The order in which you ask students to share their ideas is essential to a productive *Neriage*. First, ask those who used approach (1), the approach with the highest amount of cards, to share their idea. Then ask students who came up with approach (2), an approach which breaks down the numbers into sets of tens and ones, to share their idea. Finally, ask those who used approach (3), which uses the fewest number of cards, to share their solution. By presenting students' ideas in this order, the whole class will be able to see the logical progression and understand why they only need twelve cards.

4. Once students understand why they only need twelve cards, ask the following questions:

> Can you reduce the number of cards needed to display 1–31 if we can write on both sides of each card? What is the fewest number of cards you would need?

It may be a good idea to provide students with several cards so that they can experiment with writing numbers on both sides of each card.

5. Through trial and error working on their own, students may come up with many different ways to reduce the numbers of the cards needed to display 1–31. They may realize that the fewest number of cards may be six because if we can write on both sides of each card, we can display twelve numbers using only six cards.

6. The next step is to consider how to arrange the numbers on the cards. Students may work in pairs to explore this. Students may come up with following approaches:

(a) We need a set of 0–9 for the ones place and another 1 and 2 for the tens place.
(b) 3 and 0 should not be on the same card because then we cannot make 30.
(c) 1 and 1 should not be on the same card because then we cannot make 11.
(d) 2 and 2 should not be on the same card because then we cannot make 22.

7. Share and discuss these ideas as a class. Summarize that any combination of the numbers on each side of a card can display 1–31 as long as they satisfy the above conditions (a) through (d).

8. Build upon that conclusion and ask the following:

How can you display every day of the month using two cubes that have a single-digit number on each face?

Figure 2.2.3.04

9. This problem gives students the opportunity to deepen their understanding of base ten place value notation as well as geometry. Although CCSS dictate cube nets shouldn't be taught until Grade 6, it is possible to introduce nets by opening the cube in earlier grades (see Chapter 2.3.1). Students may work in pairs. If they have no prior experience working with cube nets, you can give them an example to use if they are having a difficult time.

10. Lead a class discussion. The class has already discussed that we need six cards, twelve faces total to display 1–31. Ask students who realized that the two cubes together also have a total of twelve faces to share this idea. There are multiple solutions to this problem. Let several students share their solutions until the

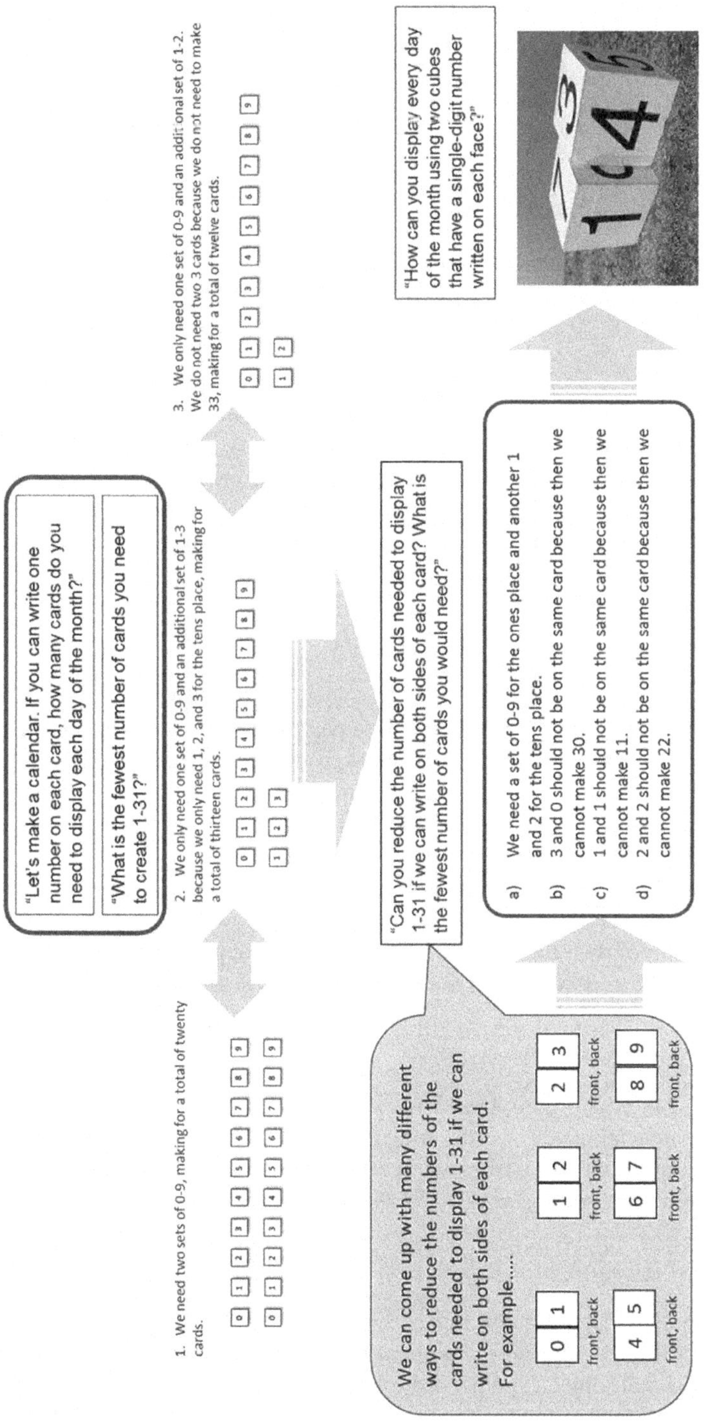

"Let's make a calendar. If you can write one number on each card, how many cards do you need to display each day of the month?"

"What is the fewest number of cards you need to create 1-31?"

1. We need two sets of 0-9, making for a total of twenty cards.

| 0 | 1 | 2 | 3 | 4 | 5 | 6 | 7 | 8 | 9 |
| 0 | 1 | 2 | 3 | 4 | 5 | 6 | 7 | 8 | 9 |

2. We only need one set of 0-9 and an additional set of 1-3 because we only need 1, 2, and 3 for the tens place, making for a total of thirteen cards.

| 0 | 1 | 2 | 3 | 4 | 5 | 6 | 7 | 8 | 9 |
| 1 | 2 | 3 |

3. We only need one set of 0-9 and an additional set of 1-2. We do not need two 3 cards because we do not need to make 33, making for a total of twelve cards.

| 0 | 1 | 2 | 3 | 4 | 5 | 6 | 7 | 8 | 9 |
| 1 | 2 |

"Can you reduce the number of cards needed to display 1-31 if we can write on both sides of each card? What is the fewest number of cards you would need?"

a) We need a set of 0-9 for the ones place and another 1 and 2 for the tens place.
b) 3 and 0 should not be on the same card because then we cannot make 30.
c) 1 and 1 should not be on the same card because then we cannot make 11.
d) 2 and 2 should not be on the same card because then we cannot make 22.

We can come up with many different ways to reduce the numbers of the cards needed to display 1-31 if we can write on both sides of each card.
For example......

| 0 | 1 | | 1 | 2 | | 2 | 3 |
| front, back | | front, back | | front, back | |

| 4 | 5 | | 6 | 7 | | 8 | 9 |
| front, back | | front, back | | front, back | |

"How can you display every day of the month using two cubes that have a single-digit number written on each face?"

Figure 2.2.3.05 Neriage Map for "Let's make a calendar"

class realizes that as long as they use number pairs which satisfy conditions (a) through (d) (see the *Neriage* Map, Figure 2.2.3.05), and make sure that each number of the number pair shows on opposite faces of a cube, their solutions will be correct.

2.2.4 *Spotlight Lesson: "Finding the Area of Triangles Inside Parallelograms"*

Grade: Upper elementary or lower secondary level

MAIN OBJECTIVE

This TTP lesson is designed to extend students' understanding of the area formula of basic figures. The lesson guides students to discover the interesting relationship between the area of opposing triangles created by bisecting diagonals in a rectangle and the area of the rectangle itself: the area of two triangles will always be half the area of the rectangle. This lesson also serves as an introduction to algebra, as students must use the distributive property in order to informally prove their conjecture. The teacher can also choose to expand upon this idea to examine if this relationship also holds true in a parallelogram.

PRIOR LEARNING REQUIRED

- CCSS.Math.Content.5.OA.A.1 "Use parentheses, brackets, or braces in numerical expressions, and evaluate expressions with these symbols."
- CCSS.Math.Content.5.OA.A.2 "Write simple expressions that record calculations with numbers, and interpret numerical expressions without evaluating them."
- CCSS.Math.Content.6.G.A.1 "Find the area of right triangles, other triangles, special quadrilaterals, and polygons by composing into rectangles or decomposing into triangles and other shapes; apply these techniques in the context of solving real-world and mathematical problems."

MAIN CCSS ADDRESSED IN THIS LESSON

- CCSS.Math.Content.6.G.A.1 "Find the area of right triangles, other triangles, special quadrilaterals, and polygons by composing into rectangles or decomposing into triangles and other shapes; apply these techniques in the context of solving real-world and mathematical problems."

RELATED LATER LEARNING

- CCSS.Math.Content.7.G.B.6 "Solve real-world and mathematical problems involving area, volume and surface area of two- and three-dimensional objects composed of triangles, quadrilaterals, polygons, cubes, and right prisms."

LESSON FLOW

1. Begin the lesson by showing Figure 2.2.4.01 which shows a rectangle divided into four parts by bisecting diagonals. You can present this problem in three different ways based on the prior experience and abilities of your class:

- If your students are not familiar with the property of rectangles, you can give them all the necessary measurements: the length and width of the rectangle as well as the location of the intersection of the diagonals.
- You can also display the rectangle on a grid to show the unit squares as shown in Figure 2.2.4.01.
- If the students are already familiar with the property of rectangles, including how diagonals bisect, you can provide them with only the measurements of the length and width of the rectangle.

2. Pick the method which is the most appropriate for your class and present the following problem:

> Find the sum of the areas of the shaded regions of this rectangle.

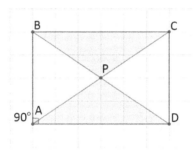

Figure 2.2.4.01

3. Have students work independently. They may find the sum of the areas of the shaded regions in several different ways:

(a) Finding the area of the two shaded regions separately by using the area formula for triangles and then adding those two amounts together.
(b) Using the area formula for triangles and realizing that the sum of the shaded area may be half of the area of the rectangle.
(c) Cutting the rectangle along the diagonals into four parts and rearranging them to find that the shaded region and the non-shaded region are congruent. (See Figure 2.2.4.02.)

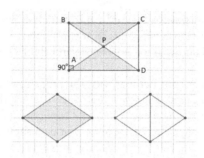

Figure 2.2.4.02

(d) Figuring out that the sum of the area of the shaded regions will be half of the area of the rectangle, without calculating the area of each triangle. (See Figure 2.2.4.03.)

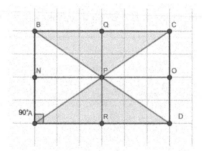

Figure 2.2.4.03

4. Begin *Neriage* by asking the students who came up with approach (a) to share their method with the class. Then, ask the students who used approach (b) to share their insight, that the sum of the shaded region might be half of the area of the rectangle. Finally, ask the students who used approaches (c) and (d) to explain how they found their answers in order to help the whole class understand that the sum of the area of two shaded regions formed by the diagonals will always be half of the area of the rectangle. These approaches put together serve as an informal proof.

5. Show Figure 2.2.4.04 and present the following problem:

Find the sum of the areas of the shaded regions of this rectangle.

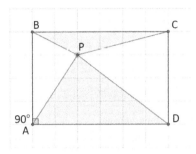

Figure 2.2.4.04

Just as in the previous problem, students may use the given measurements if necessary. Have students work independently. Again, they may try to solve the problem using approaches (a) through (d).

6. Use *Neriage* to guide students to share their ideas in a logical progression, discussing approaches (a) through (d). Help them realize that it does not matter where P is located within the rectangle, the area of the shaded regions and non-shaded regions will always be the same.

7. Guide students to examine the equations created when we plug in numbers to calculate the area of the two shaded triangles. Because they are already familiar with the distributive property of multiplication they should be able to realize on their own that:

Area of the triangle BPC: $6 \times 1 \div 2 = 3$
Area of the triangle APD: $6 \times 3 \div 2 = 9$
The sum of the triangles BPC and APD: $6 \times 1 \div 2 + 6 \times 3 \div 2 = 12$
(Equation A)
The area of the rectangle ABCD: $6 \times 4 = 24$ (Equation B)

8. By comparing equations (A) and (B), students may realize that the sum of the area of the triangles is always half of the area of the rectangle because of the distributive property:

$6 \times 1 \div 2 + 6 \times 3 \div 2$
$= 6 \times (1 + 3) \div 2$
$= 6 \times 4 \div 2$

9. Help students realize that the sum of the heights of the two shaded triangles will always be the same as the length of the vertical side of the rectangle as long as P is located inside the rectangle. Furthermore, the sum of the area of

the shaded regions of a rectangle is always half the area of the rectangle for two reasons:

- The opposite sides of a rectangle are parallel. Therefore the distance between the opposite sides, which is the sum of the heights of triangles, is always the same.
- The lengths of the opposite sides are equal. Therefore the bases of the two triangles are always equal.

10. You may want to extend this lesson to include parallelograms, if your students are familiar with the properties of parallelograms. Since parallelograms also have the above two properties, the area of two shaded triangles will be half the area of the parallelogram, as shown in the following diagram:

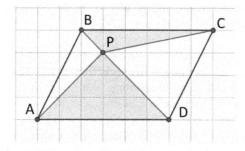

Figure 2.2.4.05

2.2.5 Spotlight Lesson: "Devising Ways to Construct a Congruent Triangle"

Grade: Lower secondary level

MAIN OBJECTIVE

In this TTP lesson students will conduct a hands-on investigation to informally determine the conditions for congruent triangles. They will be given a triangle shown actual size with all the measurements for lengths and angles. Students must devise an effective way to recreate this triangle using familiar tools, such as rulers, set squares, protractors, and compasses. The key point of this lesson is to help students figure out what are the minimum amount of measurements necessary to make a congruent triangle. Although this lesson is primarily designed for lower secondary grades according to CCSS requirements, it may also be appropriate for elementary students who are familiar with constructing basic geometric figures such as triangles and quadrilaterals using rulers, set squares, protractors, and compasses.

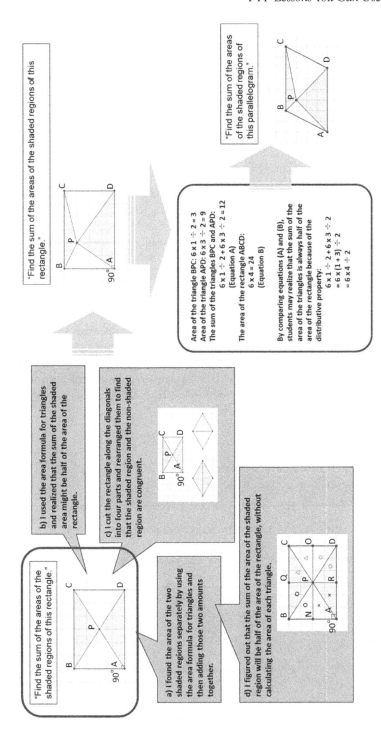

Figure 2.2.4.06 Neriage Map for "Finding the area of triangles inside parallelograms"

PRIOR LEARNING REQUIRED

- CCSS.Math.Content.2.G.A.1 "Recognize and draw shapes having speci-fied attributes, such as a given number of angles or a given number of equal faces. Identify triangles, quadrilaterals, pentagons, hexagons, and cubes."
- CCSS.Math.Content.4.MD.C "Geometric measurement: understand concepts of angle and measure angles."
- CCSS.Math.Content.4.G.A "Draw and identify lines and angles, and classify shapes by properties of their lines and angles."

MAIN CCSS ADDRESSED IN THIS LESSON

- CCSS.Math.Content.7.G.2.A.2 "Draw (freehand, with ruler and pro-tractor, and with technology) geometric shapes with given conditions. Focus on constructing triangles from three measures of angles or sides, noticing when the conditions determine a unique triangle, more than one triangle, or no triangle."

RELATED LATER LEARNING

- CCSS.Math.Content.8.G.A.2 "Understand that a two-dimensional fig-ure is congruent to another if the second can be obtained from the first by a sequence of rotations, reflections, and translations; given two congruent figures, describe a sequence that exhibits the congruence between them."
- CCSS.Math.Content.HSG.CO.B.8 "Explain how the criteria for triangle congruence (ASA, SAS, and SSS) follow from the definition of congru-ence in terms of rigid motions."

LESSON FLOW

1. Begin by giving students the triangle in Figure 2.2.5.01 and asking them to draw another one that is exactly the same (congruent).

Draw a triangle that is exactly the same as this triangle.

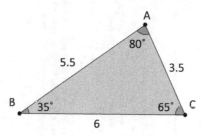

Figure 2.2.5.01

2. Have students work on their own. They will first need to think about what measurements they need. Some students may want to use all three sides, and all three angles. Some may argue that they need only some of these measurements.

3. Remind students that when they are drawing they must also note which measurements they use.

4. Encourage students to figure out what are the minimum amount of measurements they need to draw the triangle.

5. Through trial and error, students are expected to come up with a conjecture, such as only three measurements are enough to make an identical triangle. Students may have different ideas about which measurements are necessary:

(a) The lengths of all three sides, AB, BC, and AC.
(b) The lengths of two sides, AB and BC, and the angle in between ∠ABC.
(c) The lengths of two sides, BC and CA, and the angle in between ∠ACB.
(d) The lengths of two sides, AB and AC, and the angle in between ∠BAC.
(e) The length of side AB, and two angles, ∠ABC and ∠BAC.
(f) The length of side BC, and two angles, ∠ABC and ∠ACB.
(g) The length of side AC, and two angles, ∠BAC and ∠ACB.
(h) Three measurements are needed that are different than the ones listed above.
(i) Four, five, or six measurements are needed.

6. Before the *Neriage*, let each student cut out the triangle they drew and put it on top of the original triangle to see if both triangles are congruent. Have them work with partners to discuss what the minimum amount of necessary measurements are.

7. Begin *Neriage* by asking students to share what they think the minimum necessary measurements are.

8. Organize the writing on the board as shown in the *Neriage Map* for this lesson to help facilitate the discussion so students can see what the different approaches have in common. Group similar approaches together. For example, approaches (b), (c), and (d) all measure the lengths of two sides and the angle in between. Through this discussion, the class can come to the consensus that there are three different groups of minimum necessary measurements: ASA, SAS, and SSS.

THE DESIGN BEHIND THIS TTP LESSON

This lesson has been discussed among Japanese teachers and has been the subject of many research lessons since the 1980s. The success of this lesson depends on what triangle the teacher gives students to recreate. Among the many lesson plans developed during the 1980s, the following triangles were popular choices for this lesson.

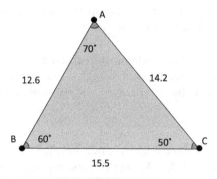

Figure 2.2.5.02

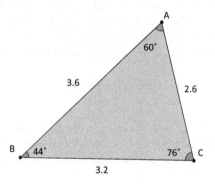

Figure 2.2.5.03

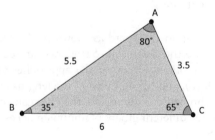

Figure 2.2.5.04

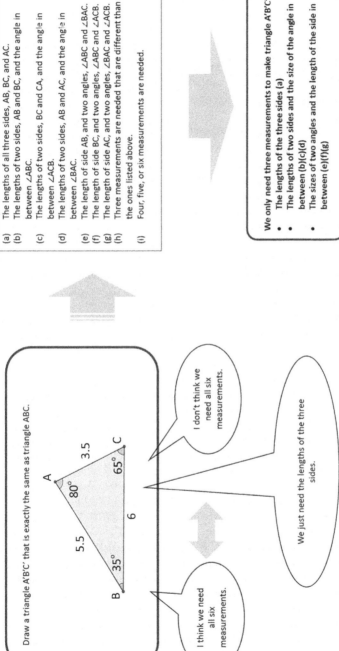

(a) The lengths of all three sides, AB, BC, and AC.
(b) The lengths of two sides, AB and BC, and the angle in between ∠ABC.
(c) The lengths of two sides, BC and CA, and the angle in between ∠ACB.
(d) The lengths of two sides, AB and AC, and the angle in between ∠BAC.
(e) The length of side AB, and two angles, ∠ABC and ∠BAC.
(f) The length of side BC, and two angles, ∠ABC and ∠ACB.
(g) The length of side AC, and two angles, ∠BAC and ∠ACB.
(h) Three measurements are needed that are different than the ones listed above.
(i) Four, five, or six measurements are needed.

We only need three measurements to make triangle A'B'C':
- The lengths of the three sides (a)
- The lengths of two sides and the size of the angle in between (b)(c)(d)
- The sizes of two angles and the length of the side in between (e)(f)(g)

Draw a triangle A'B'C' that is exactly the same as triangle ABC.

I don't think we need all six measurements.

We just need the lengths of the three sides.

I think we need all six measurements.

Figure 2.2.5.05 Neriage Map for "Devising ways to construct a congruent triangle"

The success of this lesson depends on what triangle the teacher gives students to recreate. Research has shown that there are four essential criteria:

- The triangle itself is small enough to fit in the pages of the students' notebooks.
- The triangle is big enough to be seen during the whole class discussion.
- The length of each side can be measured and made using the students' rulers; they must be rounded to the nearest tenth.
- Each angle should be a whole number so students can use their protractors.

Students must be able to make the triangle before they can discuss it. If they cannot draw it using the tools they have, it will be very difficult for them to think about what the necessary measurements are to make congruent triangles. Thus, it is crucial to give them a triangle that will be optimal for them to work with.

When you design a TTP lesson, it is critical that the task is appropriate for the students to accomplish the goal of the lesson. This lesson uses a version of the triangle which has been widely used in Japanese classrooms in recent years. This is the result of several iterations of triangles that have developed for this lesson and researched over the years since the 1980s (e.g., Fujii & Iitaka, 2011; Fujii & Majima, 2020a; Hironaka & Sugiyama, 2000; Takahashi, 1987).

2.3 TTP Lessons with Multiple Correct Solutions

This section consists of several Spotlight Lessons which detail TTP lessons featuring open-ended problems. Open-ended problems have multiple correct solutions and help students develop higher-order thinking (Becker & Shimada, 1997). In the first Spotlight Lesson of this section, "Opening a cube," students explore the various ways to open a cube into a cube net. Although there is only one answer seven cuts, the process to get the answer invites the students to explore a total of eleven different nets to make a cube. Thus, I consider this an example of an open-ended problem. In "How many different squares can you make on a geoboard?" students discover how to find all the different size squares on a 7 × 7 geoboard. In "Find all the isosceles triangles on a geoboard," they investigate how to find all the isosceles triangles with specific segment AB on a 7 x7 geoboard. "Let's create new math problems! A lesson from *Mondai kara Mondai e [From Problem to Problem]*"(Takeuchi & Sawada, 1984) is a special kind of open-ended problem in which students create new math problems based on a problem that they have already studied. These lessons range from lower elementary to lower secondary levels.

2.3.1 *Spotlight Lesson: "Opening a Cube"*

Grade: Upper elementary level

MAIN OBJECTIVE

A net is a three-dimensional shape which has been flattened into a single two-dimensional figure. In this lesson, students will investigate how they can flatten a cube into different kinds of cube nets by cutting the edges of cardboard cubes with plastic knives. During the *Neriage* for this lesson, they will examine all the different kinds of cube nets and informally determine that there are eleven nets for a cube. The *Neriage* also includes a discussion on why seven edges must be cut in order to make a cube net. Students will have to use what they have previously learned about the numbers of faces and edges of a cube in order to answer this question.

Most curricula, such as CCSS, dictate that students should investigate the attributes of basic geometric figures, such as cubes, in elementary school. It is essential that teachers not only create opportunities for students to identify the attributes of these geometric figures, such as the numbers of edges and faces, but also give them a chance to use their knowledge of the attributes to help them solve problems. This TTP lesson gives students such an opportunity, deepening their understanding of the relationship between two-dimensional and three-dimensional figures. The hands-on investigation and informal reasoning in this lesson will reinforce elementary students' understanding of geometric figures in order to prepare them to encounter geometry in secondary school.

PRIOR LEARNING REQUIRED

- CCSS.Math.Content.K.G.A "Identify and describe shapes."
- CCSS.Math.Content.2.G.A.1 "Recognize and draw shapes having specified attributes, such as a given number of angles or a given number of equal faces. Identify triangles, quadrilaterals, pentagons, hexagons, and cubes."

MAIN CCSS ADDRESSED AND EXPANDED UPON IN THIS LESSON

- CCSS.Math.Content.2.G.A.1 "Recognize and draw shapes having specified attributes, such as a given number of angles or a given number of equal faces. Identify triangles, quadrilaterals, pentagons, hexagons, and cubes."

RELATED LATER LEARNING

- CCSS.Math.Content.6.G.A.4 "Represent three-dimensional figures using nets made up of rectangles and triangles, and use the nets to find the surface area of these figures. Apply these techniques in the context of solving real-world and mathematical problems."

1. Prepare enough cubes for all the students to use during the lesson. Although some commercial products are available, such as Polydron, you can also make cubes out of two inch cardboard squares. Tape the squares into cubes with masking tape, or any tape that can be easily cut with a plastic knife. Each pair of students may want to cut at least three or four cubes, so make sure to prepare many cubes in advance. You will also need to prepare the plastic knives.

2. Begin the lesson by showing students a cube and asking the following question:

> Let's try opening up a cube and flattening it into a single two-dimensional shape by cutting some of the edges. We call such flattened shapes "nets."
>
> How many edges do you have to cut in order to flatten a cube into a net? Make sure all the faces of your net remain connected as one shape.

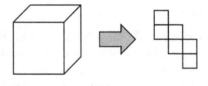

Figure 2.3.1.01

You may want to demonstrate opening a cube by cutting along the edges one by one until it is completely flat.

3. Have students work with partners. Ask them to keep a record of how many edges they cut to open each cube. Encourage them to try cutting the cubes open in various ways to help them discover different cube nets. Once they make a net, have them put that net to the side and try to open up another cube into a different net.

4. Students will come up with a variety of nets through trial and error. There are eleven different cube nets, as shown in Figure 2.3.1.02. Walk around the classroom to see if the class is finding most of the nets.

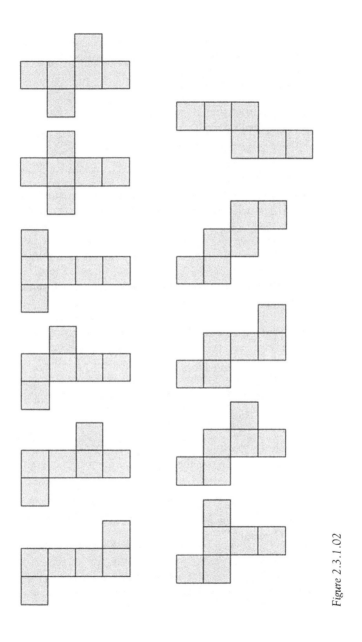

Figure 2.3.1.02

5. Begin *Neriage* by asking students to share the nets they made. Help students realize that some of the nets may look different but are actually the same because of the way they are oriented.

6. Organize the writing on the board as shown in the *Neriage* Map for this lesson to help students see there are eleven different cube nets. It may be useful to reorganize the nets into groups based on the number of faces in each column as shown in the *Neriage* Map.

7. Help students realize that they need to cut seven edges to make a net by asking the following question:

Why do we always cut seven edges of a cube to fully open it? Is it the least number of edges we can cut a cube to make it flat?

8. Let students freely share their observations about what the eleven cube nets have in common:

(a) All the nets consist of six squares.
(b) The squares are joined by five connecting edges.
(c) All the nets have fourteen exposed edges.

9. Help students discover the relationship between the number of edges in a cube and the number of edges that connect the faces of each cube net:

[12: the number of edges in a cube] – [5: the number of the edges remaining attached after opening the cube] = [7: the number of edges that must be cut]

2.3.2 Spotlight Lesson: "How Many Different Squares Can You Make on a Geoboard?"

Grade: Elementary level

MAIN OBJECTIVE

This seemingly simple task lets students conduct a hands-on investigation by asking them to construct as many different squares as they can on a 7 × 7 geoboard, as shown in Figure 2.3.2.01.

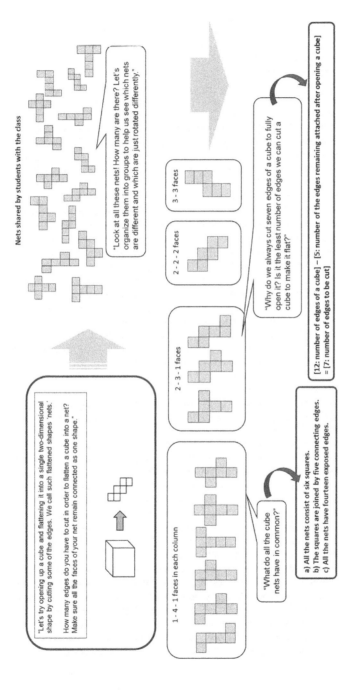

Figure 2.3.1.03 Neriage Map for "Opening a cube"

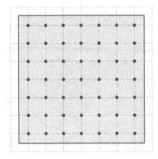

Figure 2.3.2.01

Although many children know the term "square" from their everyday lives, when a square is oriented as shown on the right in Figure 2.3.2.02 they often mistakenly call it a diamond.

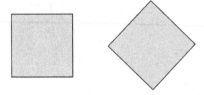

Figure 2.3.2.02

This misconception may be due to a lack of experience examining quadrilaterals to determine if they are squares. Students need to know the definition of a square and become comfortable applying it. The open-ended problem of this lesson provides that experience. Students must perform an informal investigation and use the definition of squares to test their ideas.

This lesson may be appropriate for both elementary and lower secondary grades. Students who have already learned the Pythagorean theorem can use it to find the length of the sides of the tilted squares to verify if they are different sizes. This lesson can also serve as a discussion of irrational numbers as the lengths of the sides of the tilted squares are all irrational. It should be noted that many students will think that the task in this lesson is too easy before they begin working on it. However, even college students sometimes cannot find more than six squares. This lesson can provide an interesting challenge for a variety of grade levels.

PRIOR LEARNING REQUIRED

- CCSS.Math.Content.K.G. "Identify and describe shapes."
- CCSS.Math.Content.K.G.A.2 "Correctly name shapes regardless of their orientations or overall size."

MAIN CCSS ADDRESSED AND EXPANDED UPON IN THIS LESSON

- CCSS.Math.Content.1.G.A.1 "Distinguish between defining attributes (e.g., triangles are closed and three-sided) versus non-defining attributes (e.g., color, orientation, overall size); build and draw shapes to possess defining attributes."

RELATED LATER LEARNING

- CCSS.Math.Content.8.G.B.7 "Apply the Pythagorean Theorem to determine unknown side lengths in right triangles in real-world and mathematical problems in two and three dimensions."

LESSON FLOW

1. Prepare several geoboard worksheets for each student so they can use them to record the squares they make. You can also prepare worksheets with the squares in Figure 2.3.2.03 if the class will need to review the definition of a square.

2. Begin the lesson by showing the following two shapes and asking this question:

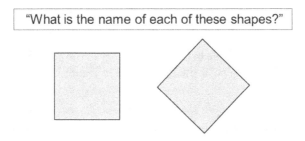

Figure 2.3.2.03

Possible student responses are:

(a) The one in the left is a square, the one on the right is a diamond.
(b) Both shapes look like squares.

Ask students to explain their reasoning. Students often make their arguments based on how they think each shape looks, whether they look the "same" or "different." This is a great opportunity to help students master a critical skill, "Correctly name shapes regardless of their orientation or overall size" (Common Core State Standards Initiative, 2010). Students need to understand that orientations are not a defining attribute of geometric figures. To help students remember this, you can ask, "What is a square?" For elementary students, a square is a geometric figure that satisfies the following three conditions:

1   It's a four-sided shape (quadrilateral).
2   All four sides are the same length.
3   All four corners are right angles.

Once the class has clarified the definition, they can then examine if both shapes satisfy all three conditions. If necessary, you can also give them worksheets of the two shapes and ask them to measure the sides and angles to determine if both shapes meet the definition of square. This reviews what they have previously learned about squares and prepares them for the main open-ended task of this lesson.

3. Give each student a 7 × 7 geoboard, rubber bands, and geoboard worksheets for recording their work. Present the following problem:

Make different size squares on your geoboard. Make as many different size squares as possible.

---

4. Walk around the classroom and remind students that the squares must be different sizes. Squares made in different sections of the geoboard are not necessarily different sizes, such as the ones shown in Figure 2.3.2.04:

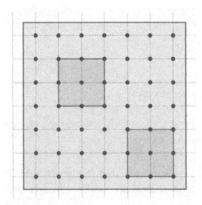

Figure 2.3.2.04

5. Some students may make the following six squares:

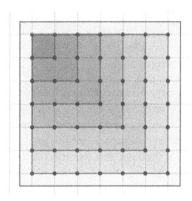

Figure 2.3.2.05

These are all the 6 square sizes that can be made which are not tilted in any way.

You may want to show these students the following shape on a geoboard and ask if it is a square or not:

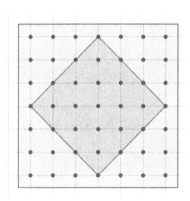

Figure 2.3.2.06

6. Students are expected to come up with a variety of different size squares. There are a total of fifteen different size squares that can be made on a 7 × 7 geoboard, six are non-tilted and nine are tilted (please refer to the *Neriage* Map for this lesson for a display of all fifteen different square sizes). Walk around to see if the class as a whole has discovered most of them.

7. Begin *Neriage* by asking students to share the shapes they made.

Ask them to prove that each shape they share is a square by showing that it satisfies all three conditions that the class agreed upon earlier:

1   It's a four-sided shape (quadrilateral).
2   All four sides are the same length.
3   All four corners are a right angle.

The class should discuss if the lengths of the sides of each square presented are different from the lengths of the sides of the squares which have already been presented. They can use a ruler or a string to compare the lengths, especially for tilted squares as their dimensions are not obvious. Students who are familiar with the Pythagorean theorem can use it to calculate the length of the sides of the titled squares. All nine tilted squares are shown in Figure 2.3.2.07.

8. After the class has shared all their squares, help them organize their squares into groups to see if they have found all the possible different size squares. You can draw students' attention to the slope of the bottom or bottom right side of each square to help them organize the squares into seven different groups (please refer to the *Neriage* Map for this lesson).

Once you've organized the squares into groups, the class can informally test to see if any other squares with the same slope but a different size can be made on the 7 × 7 geoboard.

Facilitate discussion so students can confirm that there are fifteen different squares they can make on a 7 × 7 geoboard.

9. Option to discuss irrational numbers. You can also introduce irrational numbers during *Neriage* as the tilted squares all have sides whose lengths are irrational numbers.

2.3.3 Spotlight Lesson: "Find all the Isosceles Triangles on a Geoboard"

Grade: Upper elementary and lower secondary level

MAIN OBJECTIVE

This TTP lesson is designed to extend students' understanding of isosceles triangles through hands-on investigation. Students must find all the isosceles triangles on a 7 × 7 geoboard using a given line segment AB as one of the sides. In the first task, segment AB is a horizontal line. In the second task, segment AB is sloped. Through these two tasks, students will realize what the common features are among the third vertices of these triangles. Upper elementary and lower secondary students who have already studied perpendicular bisectors and the property of circles will get the most out of this lesson, as they can use both concepts to verify if they have found all the triangles.

Even elementary students who have only learned about isosceles triangles can enjoy this lesson, although they won't be able to informally prove if they

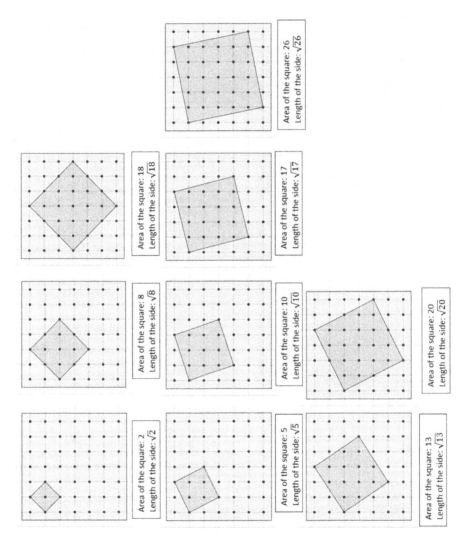

Figure 2.3.2.07

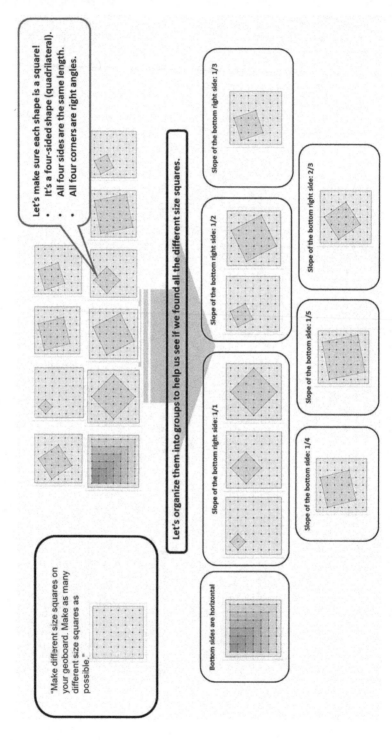

Figure 2.3.2.08 *Neriage* Map for "How many different squares can you make on a geoboard?"

have found all of them. Some students have a limited conception of isosceles triangles; they can only imagine the type of triangle shown in Figure 2.3.3.01. The location of segment AB for each task was carefully selected to help students overcome this misconception.

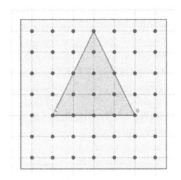

Figure 2.3.3.01

PRIOR LEARNING REQUIRED

- CCSS.Math.Content.1.G.A.1 "Distinguish between defining attributes (e.g., triangles are closed and three-sided) versus non-defining attributes (e.g., color, orientation, overall size); build and draw shapes to possess defining attributes."
- CCSS.Math.Content.2.G.A.1 "Recognize and draw shapes having specified attributes, such as a given number of angles or a given number of equal faces. Identify triangles, quadrilaterals, pentagons, hexagons, and cubes."

MAIN CCSS ADDRESSED AND EXPANDED UPON IN THIS LESSON

- CCSS.Math.Content.4.G.A.2 "Classify two-dimensional figures based on the presence or absence of parallel or perpendicular lines, or the presence or absence of angles of a specified size. Recognize right triangles as a category, and identify right triangles."
- CCSS.Math.Content.4.G.A.3 "Recognize a line of symmetry for a two-dimensional figure as a line across the figure such that the figure can be folded along the line into matching parts. Identify line-symmetric figures and draw lines of symmetry."

RELATED LATER LEARNING

- CCSS.Math.Content.7.G.A.2 "Draw (freehand, with ruler and protractor, and with technology) geometric shapes with given conditions. Focus on constructing triangles from three measures of angles or sides, noticing when the conditions determine a unique triangle, more than one triangle, or no triangle."

LESSON FLOW

1. Prepare geoboard worksheets with the AB segment for task 1 (Figure 2.3.3.02) and separate worksheets with the AB segment for task 2 (Figure 2.3.3.05). Prepare enough of each so that every student can use several to record their ideas.

2. Review the definition of an isosceles triangle by asking the class:

> What do you know about isosceles triangles?

Use student responses to clarify that, "An isosceles triangle is a triangle with two sides that are the same length."

3. Give each student a 7 × 7 geoboard, rubber bands, and several worksheets of Figure 2.3.3.02. Present the following task:

> Make an isosceles triangle ABC on the geoboard using line segment AB as one of the sides.

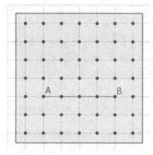

Figure 2.3.3.02

There are eight different point Cs that can make isosceles triangles ABC in this open-ended problem (Figure 2.3.3.03).

4. After students have made one isosceles triangle using segment AB, they may realize that they can make others. Encourage them to find as many as possible:

> Make as many isosceles triangles as you can using line segment AB.

There are eight isosceles triangles that students can make using line segment AB.

Note: Some of them are congruent with different orientations.

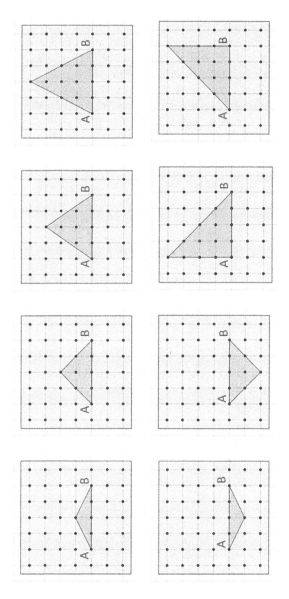

Figure 2.3.3.03

Walk around the classroom to see if students have discovered all or most of them.

5. Begin *Neriage* by asking students to share the shapes they found. Use the definition the class agreed upon earlier to examine if each of the point Cs in those shapes makes an isosceles triangle.

There are eight different point Cs that make eight different isosceles triangles ABC. Help students realize that some of the triangles are the same (congruent) even though they are oriented differently.

Encourage students to look closely and realize that two of the triangles have right angles. For one of those triangles, AB = AC, and for the second one, AB = BC. For the other six triangles, AC = BC. Put all six AC = BC triangles on a single geoboard to help students recognize that all the point Cs of the AC = BC triangles are on a line, the perpendicular bisector of AB.

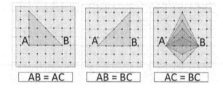

Figure 2.3.3.04

Wrap up the *Neriage* for this problem so the class can move on to the second task of this lesson.

6. Students can continue to use the same 7 × 7 geoboards. Give each student several worksheets with copies of the new segment AB on a geoboard (shown in Figure 2.3.3.05) so they can record their ideas.

Pose the second task:

> Make an isosceles triangle ABC on your geoboard using this new line segment AB as one of the sides.

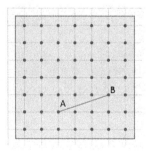

Figure 2.3.3.05

Once they have found an isosceles triangle, encourage them to make as many as possible:

Make as many isosceles triangles as you can using this new line segment AB.

---

7. The class should be able to come up with all nine triangles (please refer to the *Neriage* Map for this lesson). Note: Some of them are congruent with different orientations.

8. Begin *Neriage* by asking students to share the shapes they made. Ask the class if each of them is an isosceles triangle using the definition of isosceles that they agreed upon earlier. Students sometimes struggle to identify which two sides are the same length, so it may be a good idea to provide paper strips or strings that they can use to measure the sides.

Once they have shared their triangles, ask the following:

Do you think we have found all the possible isosceles triangles ABC on this geoboard? How can we know for sure?

---

9. Have students work in pairs or small groups to discuss if they have found all the triangles.

If students are struggling, you can suggest that they organize the triangles into the same three groups they used in the first problem of the lesson: AB = AC triangles, AC = BC triangles, and AB = BC triangles.

10. After students have had a chance to discuss their ideas in pairs or groups, you can return to *Neriage*, the whole class discussion.

Ask the class to sort the triangles into three categories: AB = AC triangles, AC = BC triangles, and AB = BC triangles.

Help students recognize what the AC = BC triangles have in common. You can put all the AC = BC triangles on a single geoboard to help students see that all the point Cs are on a line, the perpendicular bisector of AB.

Students may notice that there is no dot on the perpendicular bisector of AB other than the three point Cs of the triangles that they found as a class. Therefore, there are no other AC = BC triangles that can be made. If we extended the perpendicular bisector of AB beyond the geoboard, there may be more dots on the bisector. However, since we are only looking for triangles ABC on this geoboard, we can only make a total of three AC = BC triangles.

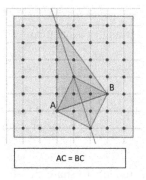

AC = BC

Figure 2.3.3.06

11. Ask students if there are any shared features among the AB = BC triangles.

Encourage students to put all the AB = BC triangles on a geoboard to help them recognize if there is any line, straight or curved, that connects all the point Cs.

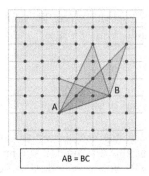

AB = BC

Figure 2.3.3.07

If they cannot imagine a curved line connecting all three Cs, you can use a dynamic geometry tool such as GeoGebra to display all the AC = BC triangles. You can draw a circle connecting the triangles (Figure 2.3.3.08) and ask:

Why are all the point Cs on the circumference?

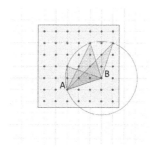

Figure 2.3.3.08

Students may be able to argue that because the BC segments of all three triangles are the same length, the distance from point B to each point C must be the same. A circumference is a collection of dots that are the same distance from the center of a circle, which in this case is point B, therefore all the point Cs must be on the circumference.

Students may look at the circumference and notice that other than the three point Cs of the triangles they made, there are no other dots available on the geoboard that could line up on the circle. Therefore, it is not possible to make any other AB = BC triangles on the geoboard.

12. Examine the AB = AC triangles in a similar fashion.

2.3.4 Spotlight Lesson: "Let's Create New Math Problems! A Lesson from the Book Mondai kara Mondai e [From Problem to Problem]"

Grade: All grade levels

MAIN OBJECTIVE

This innovative lesson was developed by Japanese researchers and educators and comes from the highly popular Japanese book *Mondai kara Mondai e [From Problem to Problem]* (Takeuchi & Sawada, 1984). It differs from other TTP lessons in that it asks students to make new problems based on a problem that they have just studied. Students can change one or multiple aspects of the original problem in order to make their new problems. Class discussion centers around categorizing the new problems into groups, how to solve them, and if they can even be solved.

This Spotlight Lesson will show how to apply this approach to the "stick problem." The "stick problem" is also covered in detail in Lesson 4 "How

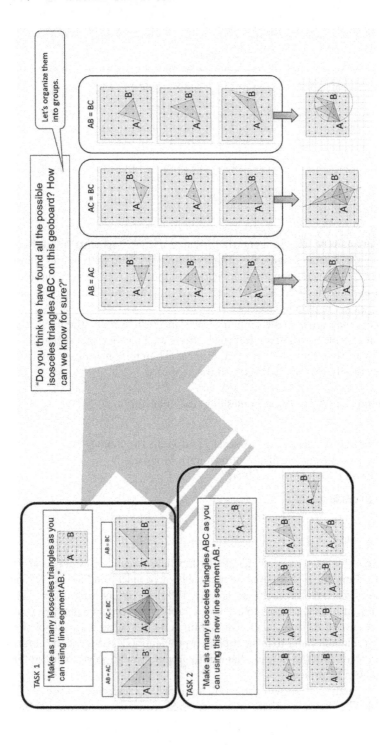

Figure 2.3.3.09 Neriage Map for "Find all the isosceles triangles on a geoboard."

many sticks are there altogether?" in Chapter 2.1. However, this "Let's create new math problems!" type of lesson can be used in any grade level to explore a variety of concepts.

According to *Mondai kara Mondai e [From Problem to Problem]*, classrooms which implement this approach report several advantages, which I have translated below:

- Students can actively engage in creating problems and critiquing problems that others make.
- Students at all levels can participate in creating a problem or problems.
- Students become more interested in mathematics.
- Students learn to enjoy the discovery of mathematics.
- Students develop the ability to apply what they have learned to other mathematics lessons.
- Teachers can design well-balanced lessons that promote both individual and whole class learning.
- Teachers can assess students' skills more broadly compared to traditional written tests which can only test students' knowledge and ability to perform procedures (Takeuchi & Sawada, 1984, pp. 21–23).

These engaging lessons will help cement and extend students' understanding of a concept. Furthermore, they provide an opportunity for students to enjoy using the mathematics they have learned.

PRIOR LEARNING REQUIRED

- CCSS.Math.Content.3.OA.D "Solve problems involving the four operations, and identify and explain patterns in arithmetic."
- CCSS.Math.Content.4.OA.A "Use the four operations with whole numbers to solve problems."
- CCSS.Math.Content.5.OA.A.1 "Use parentheses, brackets, or braces in numerical expressions, and evaluate expressions with these symbols."

MAIN CCSS ADDRESSED AND EXPANDED UPON IN THIS LESSON

- CCSS.Math.Content.4.OA.C.5 "Generate a number or shape pattern that follows a given rule. Identify apparent features of the pattern that were not explicit in the rule itself."
- CCSS.Math.Content.5.OA.A.2 "Write simple expressions that record calculations with numbers, and interpret numerical expressions without evaluating them."

RELATED LATER LEARNING

- CCSS.Math.Content.5.OA.B.3 "Generate two numerical patterns using two given rules. Identify apparent relationships between corresponding terms. Form ordered pairs consisting of corresponding terms from the two patterns, and graph the ordered pairs on a coordinate plane."

- CCSS.Math.Content.6.EE.C "Represent and analyze quantitative relationships between dependent and independent variables."

LESSON FLOW

1. Students must have spent a whole class period working on the "stick problem" before encountering this lesson. The "stick problem" is covered in detail in Lesson 4 "How many sticks are there altogether?" in Chapter 2.1. In that lesson, students have to come up with equations to determine how many sticks are required to make a row of thirty adjacent squares.

2. This Spotlight Lesson builds upon that lesson. Begin by posing the following:

"Yesterday we solved the problem, 'We will make 30 adjacent squares using sticks of the same length. How many sticks do we need?'

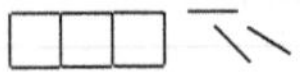

Let's make our own original problems based on this problem. Change one or more parts of this problem to make a new math problem.
If you wish, you can create several different problems."

Figure 2.3.4.01

If necessary, you can show a simple example to help students understand what "change a part of the original problem" means:

For example, you can create a problem such as, "If we make 50 adjacent squares using sticks of the same length, how many sticks do we need?"

---

3. Have each student work independently.
   Encourage students to come up with several new problems and record them in their notebooks. You can ask each student to pick their favorite problem and be ready to present it to the class during *Neriage*.
   Note that it isn't necessary that the problems the students create actually be solvable. Students often create problems with too much information or too little, problems that have too many solutions or no solutions at all. Sometimes even the problem situation may not make sense. This is ok, it is essential that students create problems freely. You can address any issues later during the

whole class discussion and help them realize that sometimes problems cannot be solved.

4. Students will create new problems by changing one or more of several elements (please refer to the *Neriage* Map for this lesson):

(a) **Changed the number**

- We will make adjacent squares using sticks of the same length. How many sticks do we need to make 50 squares?

(b) **Changed the shape**

- **b.1—Make different polygons:** We will make adjacent triangles using sticks of the same length. How many sticks do we need to make 30 triangles?
- **b.2—Made the shape 3-D:** We will make adjacent cubes using sticks of the same length. How many sticks do we need to make 30 cubes?

(c) **Changed the arrangement**

- We will make a row of squares (which do not share any sides) using sticks of the same length. How many sticks do we need to make 30 squares?

(d) **Changed the objects and/or situation**

- We will make squares using chips. How many chips do we need in order to make 30 squares?
- We will arrange square tables for a meeting. One person can sit on each side of the table. How many people can sit if there are 30 square tables?

(e) **Changed the question (switched the given number and the number to find)**

- We will make squares using sticks of the same length. How many squares can we make using 100 sticks?

Note: Students often change two or more parts of the original problem in order to make a new problem.

5. Facilitate *Neriage* by sorting the problems into groups based on what element or elements were changed. If there is time, you can also discuss if each problem is solvable. The most important discussion is how the original problem was changed in order to make new problems. Learning how to expand upon a problem to come up with new problems helps students become independent problem solvers.

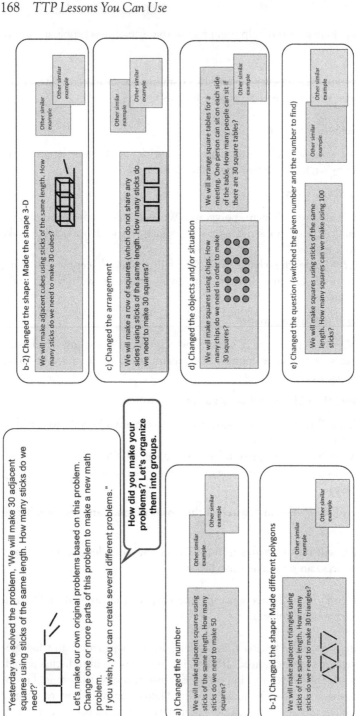

Figure 2.3.4.02 Neriage Map for "Let's create new math problems! A lesson from Mondai kara Mondai e [From Problem to Problem]"

References

Becker, J. P., & Shimada, S. (1997). *The Open-ended Approach: A New Proposal for Teaching Mathematics*. Reston, VA: National Council of Teachers of Mathematics.

Common Core State Standards Initiative. (2010). Common Core State Standards for Mathematics. Retrieved from www.corestandards.org/Math/

Fujii, T., & Iitaka, S. (2011). *Atarashii Sansuu [New Mathematics]*. Tokyo: Tokyo Shoseki.

Fujii, T., & Iitaka, S. (2012). *Mathematics International*. Tokyo: Tokyo Shoseki.

Fujii, T., & Majima, H. (2020a). *Atarashii Sansuu [New Mathematics]*. Tokyo: Tokyo Shoseki.

Fujii, T., & Majima, H. (2020b). *New Mathematics for Elementary School* (A. Takahashi & T. Watanabe, Trans.). Tokyo: Tokyo Shoseki.

Fujii, T., & Stephens, M. (2001). Fostering an Understanding of Algebraic Generalization through Numerical Expressions: The Role of Quasi-variables. Paper presented at The Future of the Teaching and Learning of Algebra, 12th ICMI study conference, Melbourne.

Gunderson, A., & Gunderson, E. (1957). Fraction Concepts Held by Young Children. *Arithmetic Teacher*, 4(October 1957), 168–173.

Hironaka, H., & Sugiyama, Y. (2000). *Atarashii Sansuu [New Mathematics]*. Tokyo: Tokyo Shoseki.

Hironaka, H., & Sugiyama, Y. (Eds.). (2006). *Mathematics for Elementary School*. Tokyo: Tokyo Shoseki.

Ministry of Education Culture Sports Science and Technology Japan. (2017). *Shougakkou gakusyuu shidou youryou kaisetu [Teaching Guide for the Course of Study, Elementary Mathematics]*. Retrieved from www.mext.go.jp/component/a_menu/education/micro_detail/__icsFiles/afieldfile/2019/03/18/1387017_004.pdf

Ministry of Education Singapore. (2006). *Mathematics Syllabus Primary*. Singapore: Ministry of Education.

National Mathematics Advisory Panel. (2008). *Foundations for Success: The Final Report of the National Mathematics Advisory Panel*. Washington, DC: National Mathematics Advisory Panel.

Takahashi, A. (1987). *Research Lesson Proposal for Congruent Triangles and Quadrilaterals*. Public research lesson proposal. Tokyo: Setagaya Elementary School attached to the Tokyo Gakugei University.

Takahashi, A., & Yanase, Y. (1997). *Pattern Block de Tsukuru Tanoshii Sannsuu Jyugyou [Fun Mathematics Lessons with Pattern Blocks]*. Tokyo: Toyokan.

Takeuchi, Y., & Sawada, T. (1984). *Mondai kara Mondai e [From Problem to Problem]*. Tokyo: Toyokan Publishing.

Thompson, P. W., & Saldanha, L. i. A. (2003). Fractions and Multiplicative Reasoning. In J. Kilpatrick, W. G. Martin, & D. Schifter (Eds.), *A Research Companion to Principles and Standards for School Mathematics* (pp. 95–111). Reston, VA: National Council of Teachers of Mathematics.

3 Designing Your Own TTP Lessons

If you want to be a pioneer of TTP in your school, you may want to start by using one of the lesson examples from Chapter 2. When you see the positive impact on your students' learning and engagement, you may want to try another. You can try out a lesson once a month as a "problem of the month." You can then gradually include more TTP lessons in between units or in addition to your existing curricula. This transition process will help both you and your students become comfortable with TTP. After a few months of this practice, your class may then be ready to use it as an integral part of their daily lessons. You can start by trying one of the mini-units from Chapter 2; each mini-unit addresses particular standards so you can use it to replace specific curriculum material.

It is also best to observe TTP lessons in action. There are some public TTP classroom videos available online, such as the ones produced by Project IMPULS International Math-teacher Professionalization Using Lesson Study (2011) and the Lesson Study Group at Mills College (2018). Lesson Study open houses, which I cover in detail in Chapter 4, are also a great opportunity to observe and discuss TTP lessons. If you have colleagues who use TTP at your school you can see its impact on students similar to your own. This may inspire you to try using the same materials. Watching an entire TTP lesson can be a powerful experience.

When you feel ready, you can use this chapter to help you craft your own TTP lessons. I outline how to choose worthwhile problems from available curriculum materials and investigate how to incorporate them in your lessons using a practice called *Kyouzai Kenkyuu*. I show you specific techniques you can use to modify these problems to create lessons that best suit your classroom. In addition, I share my strategies and a template for organizing and writing down your lesson plans. Finally, I discuss how you can use mock lessons to finalize these plans. When using this chapter to help you write your own lessons, please also refer to "Building a TTP classroom" in Chapter 1.

3.1 *Kyouzai Kenkyuu,* the Necessary Groundwork

Standards tell us what we need to teach, but not how. For example, take the following two third grade Common Core standards:

- CCSS.Math.Content.3.OA.A.1 "Interpret products of whole numbers, e.g., interpret 5 × 7 as the total number of objects in 5 groups of 7 objects each. For example, describe a context in which a total number of objects can be expressed as 5 × 7."
- CCSS.Math.Content.3.NBT.A.1 "1. Use place value understanding to round whole numbers to the nearest 10 or 100" (Common Core State Standards Initiative, 2010).

How many days do you spend teaching each standard? Which do you teach first, or should you teach them at the same time? Standards are generally too vague to use alone when writing your own TTP lessons.

Unlike the standards, textbooks provide both sequencing and pacing. Therefore, it is best to design your TTP lessons based on existing curriculum material. You can adapt these resources to make them appropriate for your classroom. Japanese teachers often say, "It may be fine to *teach the textbook* if you are a first-year teacher. However, you should aim to be someone who can teach *using the textbook* in the best way for your students." When textbook and curriculum material writers create these resources, they generally write them for first-year teachers working in an average classroom. They cannot write them with your actual classroom in mind. That is where you come in.

Japanese TTP teachers always begin designing a lesson by thoroughly researching all available related curriculum materials. This practice is called *Kyouzai Kenkyuu*, which can be translated as "the study of teaching materials" (Takahashi, Watanabe, Yoshida, & Wang-Iverson, 2005; Takahashi & Yoshida, 2004; Watanabe, Takahashi, & Yoshida, 2008). This practice helps them choose the best problems to suit their needs and gives them the necessary insight for how their students will respond so they can successfully adapt them to maximize their students' learning.

The phrase "the study of teaching materials" doesn't really cover the full scope of the practice. Japanese teachers conduct *Kyouzai Kenkyuu* when they want to teach certain subjects, investigate existing issues in their classroom, and determine if new technological tools will be useful. The full richness of *Kyouzai Kenkyuu* can be appreciated by organizing it into the three main categories of the National Research Council's instructional triangle: "mathematics," "students," and "teacher" (National Research Council, 2001, p. 314; Figure 3.1.01). These points are as follows:

Mathematics

- The mathematical content of the topic.
- Related curricula, including learning progression from prior to later grades.
- Known teaching and learning issues associated with the topic.
- Existing problem-solving activities which address the topic.
- Possible solution approaches to the problem you are considering for your TTP lesson.

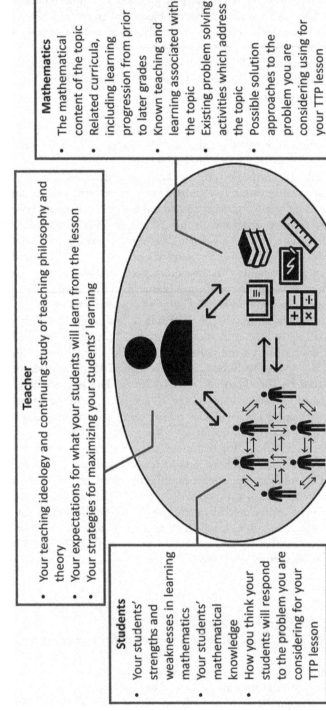

Mathematics
- The mathematical content of the topic
- Related curricula, including learning progression from prior to later grades
- Known teaching and learning associated with the topic
- Existing problem solving activities which address the topic
- Possible solution approaches to the problem you are considering using for your TTP lesson

Teacher
- Your teaching ideology and continuing study of teaching philosophy and theory
- Your expectations for what your students will learn from the lesson
- Your strategies for maximizing your students' learning

Students
- Your students' strengths and weaknesses in learning mathematics
- Your students' mathematical knowledge
- How you think your students will respond to the problem you are considering for your TTP lesson

Figure 3.1.01 Major points of *Kyouzai Kenkyuu* investigation.

Category headings "Mathematics," "Students" and "Teacher" come from the National Research Council's instructional triangle, adapted from *Adding it Up: Helping Children Learn Mathematics* (National Research Council, 2001, p. 314)

Students

- Your students' strengths and weaknesses in learning mathematics.
- Your students' mathematical knowledge.
- How you think your students will respond to the problem you are considering for your TTP lesson.

Teacher

- Your teaching ideology and continuing study of teaching philosophy and theory.
- Your expectations for what your students will learn from the lesson.
- Your strategies for maximizing your students' learning.

I will expand upon these points in a discussion of how to investigate them when conducting your own *Kyouzai Kenkyuu*.

3.1.1 Mathematics

Once you have chosen a topic for your TTP lesson or unit, you need to understand the rationale behind the available related curriculum materials. Textbooks vary in approach, depending on the ideology of the designers. The same subject may be addressed using different problems, the content arranged in different orders, and allocated different amounts of time. You can also extend your investigation to related topics taught in earlier and later grades to understand the learning progression. All this will help you understand the strengths and drawbacks of the related curricula as well as common issues encountered when teaching the topic.

Textbooks and other curriculum materials feature many interesting problems. You can often find mathematical tasks which are suitable for TTP, especially toward the end of each unit, as these problems are chosen to help students deepen their understanding of the unit content or to learn how to apply it to a different context. The National Council of Teachers of Mathematics writes:

> There are many, many problems that are interesting and fun but that may not lead to the development of the mathematical ideas that are important for a class at a particular time. Choosing problems wisely, and using and adapting problems from instructional materials, is a difficult part of teaching mathematics.
>
> (National Council of Teachers of Mathematics, 2000, p. 53)

Choosing a problem is one of the most critical and challenging tasks when designing TTP lessons, and it's often the very first step.

When you find a problem that you think will make an ideal TTP lesson, you should solve it yourself. This will help you identify the mathematical idea, or ideas, behind it, especially any interesting concepts, patterns, or relationships not made obvious by the original question. It will also help you imagine the possible solution approaches your students may take and help you determine if the problem is appropriate for your class.

3.1.2 Students

It is essential to consider the mathematics from your students' point of view. Formative assessments of your classes' prior learning related to the mathematical topic will help you understand their strengths and weaknesses. These assessments will help you better understand your individual students as well as your class as a whole. Formative assessments include tests, class observation notes, worksheets, and homework. Although this data only tells you what your students do and do not know, you can use this information to further investigate the reasons why that is and how you are going to design lessons to address your individual students' needs.

After you choose a problem for your TTP lesson and solve it yourself, you need to understand how your students will approach it and what they will learn from the experience. Schoenfeld raises several critical questions which help us understand the process of solving a specific problem from the perspective of students, such as, "What mathematical knowledge is accessible to the problem solver? How is it chosen? How is it used? Why does the solution evolve the way it does?" (1985, p. 11). You must consider all the various ways your students will approach a problem. Then you can decide whether the problem presents the right amount of challenge to inspire a mathematically rich discussion of their different approaches during *Neriage*. In most cases you will need to adapt the problem in order to make it an effective TTP lesson for your classroom. I discuss this process in detail in section 3.2 of this chapter.

3.1.3 Teacher

When designing TTP lessons, the goal is to support your students to become independent learners of mathematics. You need to make several key decisions. For example, do you want your students to work on the problem as a group? If so, how many students will there be in each group? Should the groups have students with similar skills? Are you going to make a particular manipulative available? How do you expect your students to use it? Does it help students understand the mathematics behind the problem?

A teacher must have clear expectations for what students will learn from the lesson to make these decisions. Clear expectations may include, for example, what would you expect your students to say about the topic at the end of the class? How do you want them to solve similar problems in the future? These decisions should be made based on what you learned when you researched all the related mathematics curricula and carefully considered how your students would approach the problem.

An effective TTP teacher is like a knowledgeable hiking guide who knows several routes to the destination. One route may be longer but features beautiful flowers. Another route may be too challenging for novices but offers a stunning view. A guide well-versed in the terrain can flexibly adjust the schedule and course based on the hikers' experience, physical conditions, and even the weather. In the same way, an ideal plan for a TTP lesson acts as a map of all the possible paths students may take. To create this map, teachers need a deep understanding of the topic and also the surrounding territory. *Kyouzai Kenkyuu* helps teachers gain this necessary knowledge.

3.2 Modify Existing Problems to Create TTP Lessons

Typical problems in mathematics textbooks are designed to result in a single correct answer (Becker & Shimada, 1997). These problems provide all the mathematical information needed to solve the problem in a certain way, encouraging students to take a single path to find the solution. Some students can find this route quickly, whereas others struggle. In contrast to this, TTP lesson problems should have a wider range of solution pathways so that students can take multiple approaches, or even find multiple correct answers. Classrooms whose students have a range of abilities can then attack these problems from various entry points. You can create a TTP problem by taking an existing traditional textbook problem and removing some of the given conditions or information. This opens up the problem so that students can use various approaches to solve it. You can also modify an existing open-ended problem in a similar way to make it even more open.

3.2.1 Remove Some Given Information from a Traditional Textbook Problem

Let's see how an existing problem can be adapted into a TTP lesson. The Lesson Spotlight "Finding the area of triangles inside parallelograms" from Chapter 2 was developed using this method. The original problem it was based on was a common textbook problem given to students after they had been taught the area formula for rectangles and triangles. In this problem, the students are shown a diagram of two bisecting diagonals in a rectangle which make four triangles, two of which are shaded (Figure 3.2.01). The problem asks students to find the area of the sum of the two shaded triangles.

The first step to modifying a problem into one that will work for your TTP class is always to solve it yourself. When you look at the original textbook problem, you can see that most students will find the sum of the area of the shaded triangles by recognizing that the shaded area consists of two congruent

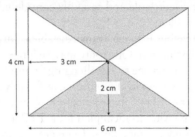

The diagram shows two diagonals inside a rectangle which make triangles. Find the area of the sum of the two shaded triangles.

Figure 3.2.01 A typical textbook problem for students who have already learned the area formulas for rectangles and triangles.

triangles (Figure 3.2.01). Since the measurements for finding the area of the triangles, the bases and heights, are given in the diagram, students will probably use the area formula for triangles to calculate the area of one triangle and then multiply that by two to find the total area of the shaded part:

The area of one of the shaded triangles: $6 \times 2 \div 2 = 6 \ (cm^2)$
The total area of the two shaded triangles: $6 \times 2 = 12 \ (cm^2)$

The measurements provided in the problem are designed for students to respond using this one straightforward solution. However, this problem has a much more interesting mathematical idea behind it.

When you solve this problem yourself, you may notice that the area of the shaded part is half the area of the rectangle, and one triangle is a quarter of the area of the rectangle:

The area of one of the shaded triangles: $6 \times 2 \div 2 = 6 \ (cm^2)$
The area of the rectangle: $6 \times 4 = 24 \ (cm^2)$

You may also realize that the total area of the non-shaded parts is also 12 cm²:

The area of one of the non-shaded triangles: $4 \times 3 \div 2 = 6 \ (cm^2)$
The total area of the two non-shaded triangles: $6 \times 2 = 12 \ (cm^2)$

Even though the shaded and the non-shaded parts are different shapes, they both have the same area. It may be interesting for students to investigate the reason why this is. If we ask them to figure out the relationship between the area of the shaded parts and the area of the rectangle, or the relationship between the area of the shaded parts and the non-shaded parts, they may be able to figure them out. If this is the objective, then students do not actually need specific measurements to investigate these relationships.

When you solve this problem yourself, you can see that it has the potential to provide an opportunity for students to use the area formula to discover a new idea: the diagonals of a rectangle divide the area of that rectangle into four equal parts. Reframing the problem in this way, rather than asking them to apply the area formula, will engage students in thinking mathematically more than just asking them to apply the area formula to given measurements. But is this challenge appropriate for your class?

When I designed the TTP lesson, "Finding the area of triangles inside parallelograms," I was hesitant to give my students this problem without providing any measurements (Figure 3.2.02). I knew that it would be much more difficult for them this way. However, they would also be more likely to discover the interesting relationship between the area of a rectangle and the areas of the shapes created by its diagonals. However, some of my students were most likely going to need some measurements to help them solve the problem. But if I gave them all the measurements, just as in the original textbook problem, most of my students would simply calculate the shaded area without realizing the relationships connecting the shapes. What I needed was a way to let some students solve the problem using calculation while also arranging the problem to provoke other solution techniques. This would generate an interesting and productive discussion of their contrasting approaches during *Neriage*.

In order to invite a variety of approaches, I decided to use a diagram which puts the rectangle on a grid (Figure 3.2.03). This way, students can

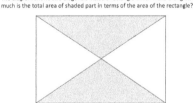

Figure 3.2.02 The area problem without given measurements.

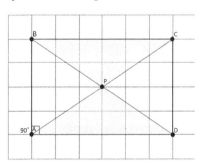

Figure 3.2.03 The area problem diagram without measurements, but also set on a grid in order to invite a variety of student approaches.

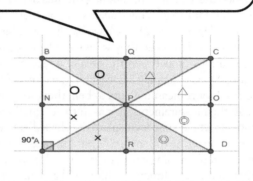

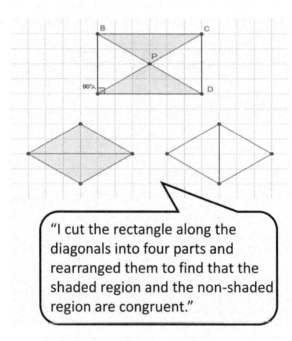

Figure 3.2.04 Examples of hands-on approaches students can use to find the relationship between the area of the shaded part and the area of the rectangle by referring to the figure on a grid instead of relying on specific given measurements.

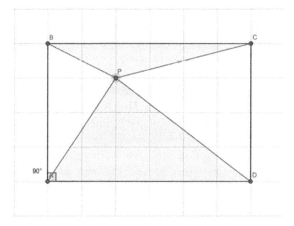

Figure 3.2.05 Changing the diagram of area problem so that the triangles are not congruent in order to extend the idea.

make calculations based on how many unit squares long the dimensions are (Figure 3.2.04). And I could make the diagram available as a worksheet for students who may want to cut out and rearrange the shaded and non-shaded parts (Figure 3.2.04). Students can also count the unit squares one by one to uncover the relationships between the areas of the shapes.

Once you have modified the problem so that it provides an appropriate level of challenge for your students, the third step is to anticipate all possible student approaches and come up with a plan for how to engage them during *Neriage*. I will further discuss how to plan *Neriage* in section 3.3 of this chapter. You can summarize "Finding the area of triangles inside parallelograms" with the concept that the sum of the area of two triangles created by the diagonals inside a rectangle will always be half of the area of that rectangle. However, you may want to extend this conclusion even further. What would happen if the shaded triangles created inside the rectangle were not congruent? Does the area of the shaded part change? (Figure 3.2.05). This may make *Neriage* more exciting. Typical textbook problems have a lot of potential for TTP lessons if you make them more open. See more discussion about this lesson, including a full *Neriage* Map, in section 2.2.4 of Chapter 2.

3.2.2 Adapting Open-Ended Problems into TTP Lessons

Nowadays, you can find more and more open-ended problems in mathematical curriculum resources. In particular, there are many hands-on activities using manipulatives to encourage students to come up with a variety of solutions through trial and error. Geoboards are one of the more popular manipulatives for students used in both elementary and middle school grades

(Gattegno, 1971). A geoboard is a square panel with several pins spaced at regular intervals (Figure 3.2.06). The most popular version has twenty-five pins in a five by five arrangement (Gattegno, 1971). There are a wide range of exciting activities using such manipulatives on the internet and in teacher resource books.

One common geoboard activity asks students to find all the different-sized squares on a twenty-five pin geoboard. This is the typical textbook activity on which the Lesson Spotlight "How many different squares can you make on a geoboard?" in Chapter 2 was based. To figure out how to modify this activity into a TTP lesson, first you have to solve it yourself. This should reveal what the challenges will be for your students and what mathematical ideas lie behind the problem. For example, most young children can easily find squares A, B, C, and D, whereas they may be unable to find squares E, F, G, and H (Figure 3.2.07). They may not recognize them because of their orientation. For those students, this problem may present a suitable challenge. "How many different squares can you make on a geoboard?" in Chapter 2 includes an in-depth discussion about how to help students overcome such misconceptions.

However, if you think most of your students will be able to find all eight squares, you can change this problem in order to engage them. You could use a geoboard with more pins, which will result in a wider variety of differently sized squares. For example, when you use a seven by seven geoboard, you can make fifteen different sized squares. That is almost twice the amount you can make on a five by five geoboard. "How many different squares can you make on a geoboard?" uses a seven by seven geoboard for this reason. It's more challenging for students to find all the squares because they cannot rely on random discovery and must investigate in an organized way.

You can develop TTP lessons based on textbook or other resource activities. They are raw material to be adapted for your classroom. Consider your students' prior learning and what will engage them. Solving the problem yourself will help you imagine what it will be like for your students to tackle it. Keep in mind that the purpose of a TTP lesson is for students to learn new mathematical ideas. Your *Kyouzai Kenkyuu* investigation will help you select a worthwhile problem and modify it so it's an appropriate challenge for your students.

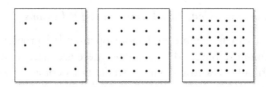

Figure 3.2.06 Examples of various geoboards.

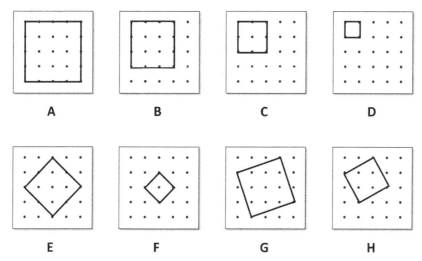

Figure 3.2.07

3.3 How to Write a TTP Lesson Plan

There is no standard way to write a TTP lesson plan, so I will share my strategy. First, I draw what I call a *Neriage* Map to show my anticipated student responses and how I want to address them during the whole class discussion. An ideal TTP lesson needs to inspire a variety of student approaches as well as be exciting. Japanese teachers have a specific term, *Yamaba*, to describe the highlight or climax of a lesson (Bass, Usiskin, & Burrill, 2002). They argue that good mathematics lessons need such moments in order to engage the students. Teachers try to design lessons in which the students experience tension, contradiction, and surprise (Mason, Burton, & Stacey, 1982). Creating *Neriage* Maps helps me ensure that my lesson will have an exciting *yamaba* moment. I also outline anticipated student responses and teacher support so that I can best guide my students throughout the lesson. I have a special template that I use for this. I then conduct a mock lesson to test my plan in which I invite my colleagues to act as the students. Their valuable feedback helps me finalize my lesson.

3.3.1 Draw a Neriage Map

Once I've chosen a problem and adapted it to best suit my students, I often start writing my lesson plan by sketching it out. This helps me to see the landscape of the problem and its potential scenarios for *Neriage*. I call these sketches *Neriage* Maps. I include *Neriage* Maps as part of the TTP lesson examples in Chapter 2. All my *Neriage* Maps include the problem, anticipated student responses, the general order in which I want students to discuss them, and a summary of what students should learn from the lesson.

I will use the third lesson from the unit "Using an equation to express a situation: A series of matchstick problems" from Chapter 2 as an example of my process for creating a *Neriage* Map. This lesson, "Find the number of dots without counting one by one" (Figure 3.3.01), teaches students they can use mathematical expressions to represent the arrangement of the dots and how to find the total number of dots without counting one by one. By comparing and discussing multiple approaches to solving the problem, students are expected to be ready to learn how to use letters to represent variables. This experience should teach students how to use mathematical expressions to represent and interpret their methods as well as apply their methods to a situation in which there are different numbers of dots per side.

To draw the *Neriage* Map for this lesson, I first solved the problem myself to come up with as many solution approaches as possible, including how I, as an adult, solved it. I used this information to help me imagine how my students

"Think about ways to count the number of dots in the picture shown. Write a math sentence for each of your methods."

"Use a mathematical expression you developed when there were only 7 dots on each side of the square to determine the total number of dots when there are 10 dots on each side."

Figure 3.3.01 The problems from "Find the number of dots without counting one by one."

For the first problem (7 dots on each side of a square)

				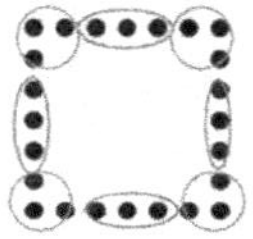	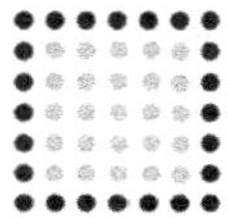
$7 \times 2 + 5 \times 2 = 24$	$7 \times 4 - 4 = 28$	$5 \times 4 + 4 = 24$	$6 \times 4 = 24$	$3 \times 8 = 24$	$7 \times 7 - 5 \times 5 = 24$

For the second problem (10 dots on each side of a square)

$10 \times 2 + 8 \times 2 = 36$	$10 \times 4 - 4 = 36$	$8 \times 4 + 4 = 36$	$9 \times 4 = 36$	$3 \times 4 + 6 \times 4 = 36$	$10 \times 10 - 8 \times 8 = 36$
$10 \times 2 + (10-2) \times 2 = 36$		$(10-2) \times 4 + 4 = 36$	$(10-1) \times 4 = 36$	$3 \times 4 + (10-4) \times 4 = 36$	$10 \times 10 - (10-2) \times (10-2) = 36$

n dots on each side of a square

$2 \times n + 2 \times (n-2)$	$4 \times n - 4$	$4 \times (n-2) + 4$	$4 \times (n-1)$	$4 \times 3 + 4 \times (n-4)$	$n \times n - (n-2) \times (n-2)$
$2n + 2n-4$ $= 4n - 4$	$4n - 4$	$4n-8+4$ $= 4n - 4$	$4n - 4$	$12 + 4n - 16$ $= 4n - 4$	$n^2-(n-2)^2$ $= n^2-n^2+4n-4$ $= 4n - 4$

Figure 3.3.02 Anticipated student responses to the dot arrangement problem.

would approach it. For example, I imagined they might look for equal groups which might help them calculate the total number of dots. They may also think that maybe since the dots are arranged in a square shape, it's important that there are four sides. However, if they simply use seven as the number of the dots on each side, they will end up counting the corner dots twice. Students may realize that they cannot simply multiply four by seven to find the answer.

Once the students figure out a way to handle the corner dots, they need to be able to represent their process. They need math sentences. I chose to present two problems in my TTP lesson example: the first has seven dots per side and the second has ten. You can decide if these values will work for your class or if you need to change them. For example, if you make the first problem ten dots per side and the second problem a hundred dots per side, this may be more exciting, because more students may come up with $10 \times 4 = 40$ for ten dots per side and $100 \times 4 = 400$ for a hundred dots per side. By tweaking the number of dots per side you also change the possible misconceptions that your students will encounter.

Once you have decided what problem(s) and what solutions your lesson will feature, you can start drawing the relationships connecting the various solutions. This will be the foundation on which your final *Neriage* Map is based. Think about which approaches students are most likely to use and which are the least likely. You may agree that most upper elementary students will calculate $7 \times 2 + 5 \times 2 = 24$, and are very unlikely to try $7 \times 7 - 5 \times 5 = 24$ (Figure 3.3.02). Consider the relationships between these approaches and how to lead the whole class discussion so students can understand the ideas behind each approach and how to represent them using mathematical expressions. You can also discuss why 7×4 doesn't work. It may be possible to draw several different versions of *Neriage* Maps.

I have drawn up one potential *Neriage* Map (Figure 3.3.03). It includes the problem and the many paths I expect my students will take to find the answer. I have organized their responses using Type 2 *Neriage* to help students compare and contrast them during the whole class discussion (please refer to Chapter 1 for a detailed discussion of the types of *Neriage*). I also included an extension problem to give students an opportunity to test their ideas. As always, I included the lesson summary, the concept that all students should understand by the end of the discussion. In this way, I have drawn a *Neriage* Map which covers all the main paths to the intended destination.

3.3.2 Outline Anticipated Student Responses and Teacher Support

When you write a lesson plan, you may be tempted to write it as a series of questions and answers between the teacher and students, such as, Teacher → Student → Teacher → Student. However, such scripts will not serve you well.

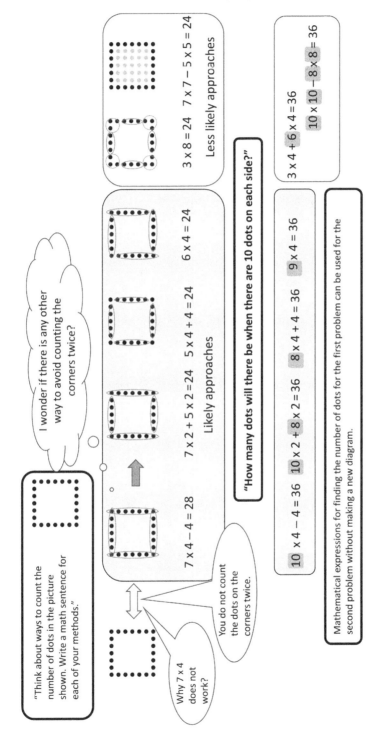

Figure 3.3.03 A *Neriage* Map for "Find the number of dots without counting one by one."

Steps, questions from the teacher, activities, and anticipated student responses	Support from the teacher	Check understanding
1. Introduction (about 3 - 5 min)		
2. Pose the problem (about 5 - 7 min)		
3. Solve the problem (about 7 - 10 min) Anticipated Student Responses		
4. Compare and discuss (about 20 - 25 min)		
4. Summarize (about 5 - 10 min)		

Figure 3.3.04 Lesson plan template.

Outlining a single narrow path in this way does not allow for enough flexibility to engage students in mathematical discourse. I have included the template that I used to write the TTP lesson examples in this book (Figure 3.3.04).

The left column of my template has the heading, "Steps, questions from the teacher, activities, and anticipated student responses" (Figure 3.3.04). To fill this section out, you must decide how to pose the problem, or problems, of the day. Experienced Japanese teachers understand the importance of posing problems so that they inspire fruitful discussion. One of my mentors once told me, "The best way to get your students to talk more about mathematics is for you, the teacher, to stop talking. You only want to ask a few thought-provoking questions." Japanese educators call such questions *Hatsumon*. Your problem(s) of the day, or *Hatsumon*, should inspire mathematical curiosity and discovery in your students. Your TTP lesson plan should include your *Hatsumon*, followed by a list of anticipated student responses. Please refer to the lessons in Chapter 2 for examples.

The amount of time you allocate for each section is important because we always have a limited amount of class time. My template is designed for a 50-minute class (Figure 3.3.04). You may want to adjust it depending on your schedule or the lesson topic. I conducted a study on TTP teaching in Japan which showed that novice teachers tend to give more time to solving a problem, while experienced teachers devoted more time to the whole class discussion (Takahashi, 2011). The point of giving students time to work on their own is so that they can share their experiences during the discussion.

The second and third columns of my template, "support from the teacher" and "check understanding," go hand in hand. Polya writes that a teacher should carefully monitor their class and when necessary, "help the student naturally . . . ask a question or indicate a step that could have occurred to the student himself" (Polya, 1945, p. 1). Therefore, the teacher needs to anticipate the help that some students may need and write this as part of the lesson plan in the second column, "support from the teacher." The third column, "check understanding," is a space to write questions you can ask to determine if students need help.

3.3.3 Conduct a Mock Lesson

After completing a *Neriage* Map and a lesson plan, Japanese teachers often conduct a mock lesson, inviting their colleagues into their classroom. The colleagues act as the students and the teacher conducts the lesson in order to find and fix any loose ends. When you ask your colleagues to participate in a mock lesson, it's best to first tell them what your goals are for the lesson. I recommend using the TRU math framework as a rubric for evaluating and providing lesson feedback (Schoenfeld & The Teaching for Robust Understanding Project, 2016). This framework outlines five key aspects of ideal classroom activity: "content," "cognitive demand," "equitable access," "agency," "authority and identity," and

" formative assessment" (Schoenfeld & The Teaching for Robust Understanding Project, 2016). Their rubric and guides are available to download from their website (Schoenfeld & The Teaching for Robust Understanding Project, 2016). These criteria will help you create and discuss effective TTP lessons.

Mock lessons generate authentic, real-time feedback from your colleagues. For example, when you pose the problem of the day, the "students" may respond, "I might not be able to understand the question when you ask it like that," or "I can't easily see the diagram you put on the board from my seat." You can stop the mock lesson at any time to take their suggestions. Teachers make many final decisions during these mock lessons, such as, how they will write on the board, how they will incorporate visual aids and manipulatives, and how they will arrange their students' desks. It may be difficult to find time to conduct mock lessons on a regular basis. However, you can try them as part of the Lesson Study practice I share in Chapter 4.

References

Bass, H., Usiskin, Z. P., & Burrill, G. (Eds.). (2002). *Studying Classroom Teaching as a Medium for Professional Development. Proceedings of a U.S.–Japan Workshop (July 31–August 6, 2000)*. Washington, DC: National Academy Press.

Becker, J. P., & Shimada, S. (1997). *The Open-ended Approach: A New Proposal for Teaching Mathematics*. Reston, VA: National Council of Teachers of Mathematics.

Common Core State Standards Initiative. (2010). Common Core State Standards for Mathematics. Retrieved from www.corestandards.org/Math/

Gattegno, C. (1971). *Geoboard Geometry*. United States: Educational Solutions.

Lesson Study Group at Mills College. (2018). Teaching through Problem Solving in Action. Retrieved from https://lessonresearch.net/teaching-problem-solving/ttp-in-action

Mason, J., Burton, L., & Stacey, K. (1982). *Thinking Mathematically*. London: Addison-Wesley Publishing.

National Council of Teachers of Mathematics. (2000). *Principles and Standards for School Mathematics*. Reston, VA: National Council of Teachers of Mathematics.

National Research Council. (2001). *Adding it Up: Helping Children Learn Mathematics*. Washington, DC: National Academy Press.

Polya, G. (1945). *How to Solve It: A New Aspect of Mathematical Method*. Princeton, NJ: Princeton University Press.

Project IMPULS International Math-teacher Professionalization Using Lesson Study. (2011). Lesson Study Library. Retrieved from www.impuls-tgu.org/en/library/index.html

Schoenfeld, A. H. (1985). *Mathematical Problem Solving*. Orlando, FL: Academic Press.

Schoenfeld, A. H., & The Teaching for Robust Understanding Project. (2016). An Introduction to the Teaching for Robust Understanding (TRU) Framework. Retrieved from http://map.mathshell.org/trumath.php or http://tru.berkeley.edu.

Takahashi, A. (2011). The Japanese Approach to Developing Expertise in Using the Textbook to Teach Mathematics Rather than Teaching the Textbook. In Y. Li & G. Kaiser (Eds.), *Expertise in Mathematics Instruction: An International Perspective* (pp. 197–219). New York: Springer.

Takahashi, A., Watanabe, T., Yoshida, M., & Wang-Iverson, P. (2005). Improving Content and Pedagogical Knowledge through Kyozai Kenkyuu. In P. Wang-Iverson & M. Yoshida (Eds.), *Building Our Understanding of Lesson Study* (pp. 101–110). Philadelphia, PA: Research for Better Schools.

Takahashi, A., & Yoshida, M. (2004). How Can We Start Lesson Study? Ideas for Establishing Lesson Study Communities. *Teaching Children Mathematics*, 10(9), 436–443.

Watanabe, T., Takahashi, A., & Yoshida, M. (2008). Kyozaikenkyu: A Critical Step for Conducting Effective Lesson Study and Beyond. In F. Arbaugh & P. M. Taylor (Eds.), *Inquiry into Mathematics Teacher Education* (Vol. 5, pp. 131–142). Houghton, MI: Association of Mathematics Teacher Educators (AMTE).

4 How TTP and Collaborative Lesson Research Can Change Your School

I offer Collaborative Lesson Research (CLR) as a professional development practice based on *Jyugyou Kenkyuu* that can help you and your school adopt TTP and create meaningful changes in teaching and learning (Takahashi & McDougal, 2016). Japanese educators have been using *Jyugyou Kenkyuu* as the main system of professional development since the establishment of the Japanese public school system (Makinae, 2019). It is credited with students' high-performance rates in mathematics and science (e.g., Lewis, 2000; Lewis, Schaps, & Watson, 1995; Lewis & Tsuchida, 1997, 1998; Stigler & Hiebert, 1999; Yoshida, 1999). These high performance rates, reported in various studies such as the Second International Math Study (Travers & Westbury, 1989) and The Third International Math and Science Study (Mullis et al., 1997), have been attracting U.S. researchers' interest in Japanese classrooms (e.g., Becker & Miwa, 1987; Becker & Shimada, 1997; Becker, Silver, Kantowski, Travers, & Wilson, 1990; Stevenson, 1980; Stevenson & Stigler, 1992). As a result, *Jyugyou Kenkyuu*, usually translated as "Lesson Study," has been a focus of global attention in the field of mathematics education since the late 1990s among teachers of mathematics hoping to address teaching and learning issues in their schools.

However, international attempts at Lesson Study have met with varying degrees of success. They are often very different from actual *Jyugyou Kenkyuu* as it is practiced in Japan (Fujii, 2014; Takahashi & McDougal, 2016). To address this issue, I developed CLR based on a deep understanding of *Jyugyou Kenkyuu* as well as extensive experience and knowledge of what specific kinds of support schools outside of Japan need to run a successful program (Takahashi & McDougal, 2016). This chapter will walk you through how to initiate and run CLR at your school. Unlike other professional development programs which are often orchestrated from the top-down and require the hiring of outside help, CLR is a grass roots effort, a collaboration of fellow teachers. You can start with just a small team of enthusiastic colleagues. Eventually, with the support of your administration, you can start conducting school-wide CLR. This will not only improve your own ability to teach using TTP, but help all teachers of mathematics in the school meet current demanding standards for teaching children how to think mathematically. Recent case studies have shown the dramatic effects of CLR. You can change your classroom and change your school.

4.1 *Jyugyou Kenkyuu,* Japan's Professional Development Program

In Japan, *Jyugyou Kenkyuu* is typically a school-wide professional development practice across all subjects (Takahashi, 2014b). It is how Japanese mathematics teachers hone their TTP expertise. Teachers design and host live research lessons taught to their regular students in their own classroom, to which they invite their colleagues to come observe and discuss.

Japanese schools and teachers use *Jyugyou Kenkyuu* to plan, examine, and improve curriculum and instruction. First, the teacher who will host the research lesson will spend weeks conducting *Kyouzai Kenkyuu* to help them choose their research lesson topic: a new teaching idea, problem-solving task, strategy, or tool (see Chapter 3 for a discussion on *Kyouzai Kenkyuu)*. This research lesson will also typically be aligned with a broader long-term learning goal, or "research theme," which the school has set for all its students for two to three years, if not longer (Takahashi & McDougal, 2016). During the research lesson, colleagues come to observe and collect data. Immediately afterward there is a post-lesson discussion in which everyone shares their valuable feedback. The conclusions drawn from the post-lesson discussion are often distributed later in some way in order to contribute to the teaching community.

4.2 Using CLR at Your School to Implement TTP

Unlike other forms of Lesson Study outside Japan, CLR includes all the crucial elements of *Jyugyou Kenkyuu* as well as necessary support for teachers working outside of Japan's established *Jyugyou Kenkyuu* system (Figure 4.2.01). We have identified CLR as having the following six components:

1　A clear research purpose.
2　*Kyouzai Kenkyuu,* the "study of teaching materials."
3　A written research proposal.
4　A live research lesson and discussion.
5　Knowledgeable others.
6　Sharing of results (Takahashi & McDougal, 2016).

CLR teachers use *Kyouzai Kenkyuu* to design research lesson proposals, which include the lesson plan, how the lesson fits into the unit, and the rationale for the lesson design. A research lesson proposal should also be aligned with a long-term research theme that will help you inspire and rally other teachers to participate in CLR. For teachers new to CLR, it is best to invite and consult "knowledgeable others," mathematical pedagogy experts, to help you conduct *Kyouzai Kenkyuu* and provide final comments during your post-lesson discussion. In this section, I will describe how to accomplish each of our six components of CLR in detail. I will also give advice on how to organize teams and schedules so you can run a successful program. In addition, I include several resources and organizations that can help you implement CLR and TTP at your school and in your community.

We have developed and refined CLR based on years of experience. For example, in America, we have been helping schools conduct CLR at eight schools in Chicago, four in San Francisco, and one in Oakland. I have acted as a knowledgeable other providing CLR support at 246 research lessons between January 2016 and January 2020 at schools in Chicago, San Francisco, Oakland, St. Louis, New York, England, Brazil, Qatar, and other countries. Due to the success of the programs, we continue to expand our efforts. This book can serve as a guide to help you establish CLR at your own school.

4.2.1   *Organize a Team*

First, you will need to choose your team. Although you may want to make CLR a school-wide endeavor, it may be more realistic to start by assembling three to five enthusiastic teachers from your school to design and teach a research lesson together. Your team can all be teachers from the same grade, but this is not necessary. A team made up of teachers from different grades would also be powerful as members would bring a more diverse view to teaching topics.

If you have more than six teachers who are interested, you can organize into two or more teams. Each team designs their own unique research lessons with the same long-term goal, or research theme, in mind. Teams could represent different grade levels and invite each other to their research lessons, bringing additional fresh perspectives to the observation and discussion (Figure 4.2.02). If you have more than three teams, you can ask each team to send a representative to form a CLR steering committee. Although CLR is a teacher-led initiative, if administrators join the steering committee it will help you receive support from your school and district. This can also help you ultimately move toward implementing school-wide CLR. I discuss more about how to schedule school-wide CLR in section 4.2.8 of this chapter, "Organizing school-wide CLR."

4.2.2   *Set a Long-Term Goal, or "Research Theme"*

Before you and your team start designing your first lesson, you must decide on a broad long-term teaching and learning goal that goes beyond any single topic or grade. This goal is called a "research theme." "Implementing TTP" is not specific enough for a research theme. A research theme describes a skill you want students to develop, and a way for them to achieve proficiency in that skill.

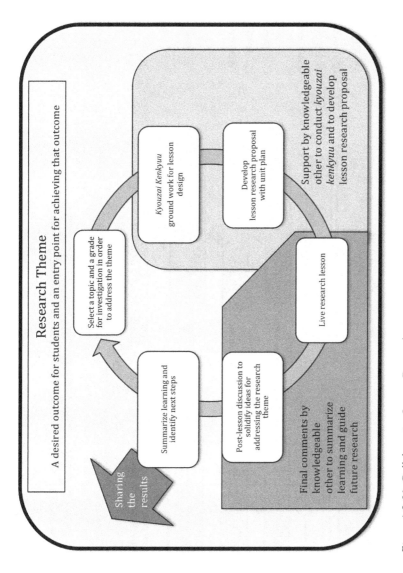

Figure 4.2.01 Collaborative Lesson Research.
Reprinted from Takahashi & McDougal (2016, p. 521)

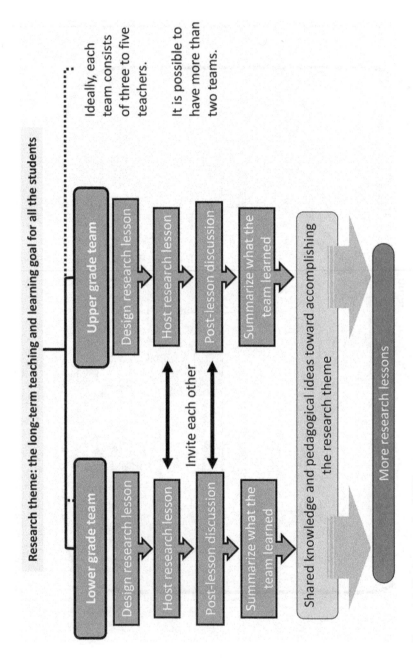

Research theme: the long-term teaching and learning goal for all the students

Ideally, each team consists of three to five teachers.

It is possible to have more than two teams.

Upper grade team

Design research lesson

Host research lesson

Post-lesson discussion

Summarize what the team learned

Invite each other

Lower grade team

Design research lesson

Host research lesson

Post-lesson discussion

Summarize what the team learned

Shared knowledge and pedagogical ideas toward accomplishing the research theme

More research lessons

Figure 4.2.02 An example of CLR team organization.

You can determine the proficiency you want your students to develop by choosing one or two "varieties of expertise" from the Common Core State Standards (2010). For example, do you want your students to use their prior learning to find solutions to new problems by themselves, or to be able to discuss with peers how to come up with a better approach to a problem by critiquing each other's solutions? Once you've picked a proficiency or two you want your students to develop, you can complete your research theme by choosing what technique will help them accomplish this. For example, John Muir Elementary School in San Francisco chose "Students will use evidence to reason and construct viable arguments so that they are confident, independent learners" for their 2018 school year research theme. A good research theme is key for driving motivation and propelling long-term CLR efforts. Teachers are eager to work together to help their students overcome the issue highlighted by the research theme.

4.2.3 *Use* Kyouzai Kenkyuu *to Develop a Research Lesson Proposal*

CLR stands for Collaborative Lesson Research, emphasis on the "research." We chose the term "CLR" based on Catherine Lewis's original description of *Jyugyou Kenkyuu* as teacher-led research (Lewis & Tsuchida, 1997). Teachers use *Kyouzai Kenkyuu*, an investigation of curricula and materials, to write their lesson plan for the research lesson they will host (Watanabe, Takahashi, & Yoshida, 2008). This detailed lesson plan will be the main part of a research lesson proposal, which ties the lesson plan into the unit as well as the research theme. The research lesson proposal must also detail the rationale for each of the choices that went into designing the lesson plan (Fujii, 2016; Takahashi, 2014b). This process requires a considerable amount of time. Japanese teachers typically meet for one or two hours three or four times to develop a research lesson proposal (Murata & Takahashi, 2002). Some schools in Chicago meet once a week for eight weeks. In addition to the lesson examples in Chapter 2 of this book, there are also several resources available for teachers on the topic of this process (e.g., Lesson Study Alliance, 2020; Lesson Study Group at Mills College, 2018; Lewis & Hurd, 2011; Project IMPULS International Math-Teacher Professionalization Using Lesson Study, 2011).

When you try designing a TTP lesson for the first time with your colleagues, I recommend that you do not attempt to create a lesson or unit from scratch. Rather, I suggest that your team chooses a TTP lesson from Chapter 2 and designs a research lesson proposal based on how you can adjust that lesson to best suit your students' needs. Please refer to Chapter 3 for guidance on how to use *Kyouzai Kenkyuu* to choose a learning goal that is appropriate for your students.

A typical research lesson proposal may include the following:

1   Lesson title.
2   Brief description of the lesson.

3   Lesson goals.
4   Relationship of the lesson to the standards: How this lesson will develop new ideas based on prior learning in terms of specific standards.
5   Background and rationale: Why the team decided to choose this lesson to investigate as a research lesson.
6   What the students are expected to learn in this lesson/unit according to the standards or curriculum.
7   Students' strengths and weaknesses observed in the past as related to the topic.
8   How this research lesson is expected to contribute to the school's research theme.
9   Consideration for designing the unit (findings from *Kyouzai Kenkyuu*): Research findings, including findings from primary and alternative curricula, and consideration of materials that might be used to facilitate learning.
10   About the unit and lesson: How the unit and lesson are designed to help students meet both content and process standards, such as Common Core State Standards Initiative (2010).
11   Unit flow: Shows how the lesson fits into a larger unit. Briefly describes what students learn before and after the lesson. You can clarify which part is the research lesson by setting the font to "bold."
12   Detailed lesson plan for the lesson (a.k.a. the lesson plan for the research lesson). Please refer to section 3.3 in Chapter 3.
13   Evaluation: Often includes questions that the team hopes to explore through the research lesson observations and post-lesson discussion. May also include a plan for summative assessments.

This outline is based on the free template available for download from the Lesson Study Alliance website (www.lsalliance.org/resources).

4.2.4 Invite Knowledgeable Others

It would be ideal for a team to have access to two knowledgeable others who are familiar with mathematical content and pedagogy (Takahashi & McDougal, 2016). You need one expert to guide you as you conduct *Kyouzai Kenkyuu* and help you develop a research lesson proposal, and another expert to provide final comments during the post-lesson discussion. District resource people, such as curriculum coordinators or content specialists, and university instructors can act as ideal knowledgeable others. You may also wish to reach out to the following professional organizations:

• World Association of Lesson Studies (www.walsnet.org).
• Mills College Lesson Study Group (https://lessonresearch.net).
• Lesson Study Alliance (www.lsalliance.org).

- Project IMPULS (www.impuls-tgu.org/en).
- Collaborative Lesson Research UK (www.collaborative-lesson-research.uk).

All these organizations provide resources as well as conduct workshops and/ or conferences.

4.2.5 Research Lesson

After your weeks of preparation and planning, you are now ready to host your research lesson. Data collected from colleagues' lesson observations will allow you to examine how effectively your desired curriculum is actually being implemented. Although teachers see their students in action every day, it's difficult for them to closely observe every single student because they are busy teaching the class. In contrast, research lessons provide a valuable opportunity for collecting feedback on how your students learn. Even though many events happen simultaneously during a lesson, multiple eyes can take notes from a wide range of perspectives. These powerful observations are then shared immediately afterwards in the post-lesson discussion.

Research lesson observers will be able to contribute more meaningful feedback if they understand the goals of your research lesson. What does your team expect the students to learn through solving the problem you chose? Why did you pick that problem? How do you want your students to overcome the challenges they will face? The best way to prepare observers for your research lesson is to share your research lesson proposal beforehand and pick out a few such critical questions to be addressed using the observation data. CLR teams often set aside time for the participants to read through the research lesson proposal before the research lesson.

Ask observers to jot down notes on what students said or did, how they struggled, and how they came up with new ideas during the lesson. It is best to include both names and times in the notes. You can also ask them to photograph students' work during the lesson, as they tend to erase their work as they try out different things. All notes and records are valuable data and make for a productive post-lesson discussion. There are also applications available which can help you take notes. For example, LessonNote, an iPad app developed by the Lesson Study Alliance specifically for conducting CLR, may be helpful for collecting data. You can learn more about LessonNote at www.lsalliance.org/lessonnote.

4.2.6 Post-Lesson Discussion

During the post-lesson discussion, everyone discusses the impacts of the lesson on student learning and how the lesson design contributed to that learning. Observers share the data they collected as well as what that data tell them, such as the advantages and disadvantages of the chosen problem(s), questions asked, materials used, and pedagogical decisions made by the teacher. Ideally, the discussion should follow immediately after the research lesson. The purpose of the discussion is not to decide whether the lesson was good or bad. Rather, participants share what they learned from the team's effort. Thus, it is critical to have an experienced post-lesson discussion moderator, as not many teachers have experienced this kind of discussion before.

This moderator should be someone not on the planning team, who helps focus the discussion and keeps the conversation grounded in data. They help identify the critical issues of the research lesson and call on participants to share their thoughts. The moderator guides discussion to help the group come up with ideas of how to improve teaching and learning on the topic of the lesson. They make sure the questions raised by the planning team in their research lesson proposal are addressed, and help the group come to a consensus on the answers.

You will need to schedule about thirty minutes to an hour for the main part of the discussion and another ten to forty minutes for final comments by a knowledgeable other. This final commentator wraps up the post-lesson discussion by using concrete examples from the research lesson to derive new teaching and learning knowledge. They highlight specific events from the lesson to show how teaching theory works in practice. This also serves as a model on how to observe students in the classroom and reflect on lessons. The moderator is also there to outline a clear road map for how teachers can advance the school's research based on what was learned from the research lesson. In this way, they summarize the post-lesson discussion as well as suggest next steps (Seino & Foster, 2020; Takahashi, 2014a).

4.2.7 Summarize Learning

To wrap up a round of CLR, you need to summarize what you learned from the research lesson and share it with your teaching community. After the post-lesson discussion, team members should have a meeting to summarize what they learned. Some U.S. schools write up a few pages for their school's newsletter and distribute it to everyone, including teachers who were not able to attend. Japanese schools often compile all their research lesson proposals and summaries from the school year into a booklet they share with their school as well as neighboring schools. Some Japanese schools, such as Sakamoto Elementary School (discussed in section 1.3 of Chapter 1), publish their collection of *Jyugyou Kenkyuu* findings as a book (Takahashi & Yoshida, 2004).

4.2.8 Organizing School-Wide CLR

With school-wide support, CLR can serve as the framework to make systemic changes toward improving teaching and learning at your school. Most elementary schools in Japan and some in the U.S. are using school-wide Lesson Study to successfully implement TTP lessons as the primary teaching

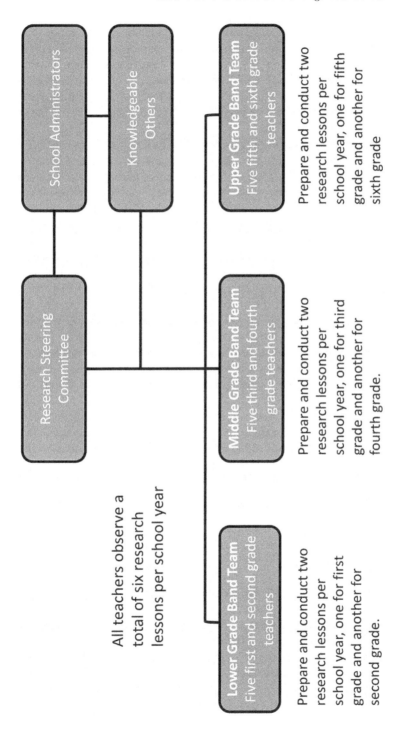

Figure 4.2.03 Example of how to schedule school-wide CLR in an elementary school with three teams.

approach for mathematics in all grades. Almost all of these schools have a research steering committee and positive involvement and support from administrators. The steering committee is made up of representatives from each CLR team in the school. Each school has three or more teams, depending on the size of the school. And in each school, the entire staff is working toward their research theme, their long-term teaching and learning goal. This massive effort requires serious dedication and organization. What do their CLR schedules look like?

To examine how to organize school-wide CLR, let's take as an example of an elementary school that has two classes in each grade from first to sixth grade. Let's say that there are a total of fifteen teachers participating, including both classroom and special subject teachers. The school divides these fifteen teachers into three teams, one to investigate each grade band: lower, middle, and upper (Figure 4.2.03). Each team will design and conduct two research lessons a year, perhaps one in fall and one in spring. Three teams teaching two lessons a year means that six teachers will conduct a total of six lessons in a year. The next year, a different six teachers will have the opportunity to host research lessons. In three years, all the teachers would have had a chance to teach a research lesson. Even though each teacher is only hosting one research lesson over the course of three years, they are still working with their team to design and develop six research proposals during that time. In addition to these learning experiences, each teacher will also have the chance to observe and discuss six research lessons on the topic of the school's research theme every year, therefore participating in eighteen research lessons over the course of three years.

For CLR on this scale, school administrators need to allocate six half-days a year for the teachers to host their research lessons and post-lesson discussions. Each team also needs ideally about eight hours of common preparation time over a four- to eight-week period to develop each research lesson proposal. The following is an example meeting schedule for a team's development and hosting of a research lesson:

- **The beginning of the school year:** Decide on the topic of the research lesson and who will teach it. Each team member agrees to start thinking about a rough idea for the lesson and to conduct their own *Kyozai Kenkyuu* related to the topic. The steering committee and the school administrators may also need to consult with each team to create the research lesson schedule for the school year.
- **Five weeks before the research lesson:** Each member shares their ideas for the research lesson based on their individual *Kyouzai Kenkyuu*. The teams decide on what lesson they will develop into a research lesson proposal.
- **Four weeks before the research lesson:** Develop the first draft of the lesson plan.
- **Three weeks before the research lesson:** Discuss potential rewrites of the lesson plan.

- **Two weeks before the research lesson:** Decide the problem to be used for the research lesson and update the lesson plan draft.
- **One week before the research lesson:** Finalize the research lesson proposal and send it to the invited final commentator of the research lesson, a knowledgeable other. The school's research theme, the research lesson's grade level, topic, and rationale should all be finalized at this point.
- **A few days before the research lesson:** Conduct a mock lesson asking the team members to act as "students" in order to uncover and resolve any loose ends, such as making sure the key questions are engaging and the board writing is effective, including visual presentations of key questions and mathematical representations such as diagrams and equations.
- **The day before the research lesson:** Print the lesson plan and distribute it to the teachers of the school. Prepare the materials you will use during the research lesson, such as manipulatives, posters, and worksheets.
- **The day of the research lesson:** Conduct the research lesson and post-lesson discussion. One of the team members should take notes during the post-lesson discussion. These notes will be used later when the team summarizes their learning from the post-lesson discussion.
- **Within a week of the research lesson:** Summarize what was learned from the post-lesson discussion and decide how to distribute the findings.

4.3 Advantages of CLR

CLR is an ideal professional development program to improve teaching and learning at your school. Tests may be able to measure what students did or didn't learn, but they cannot explain why. In contrast, the live research lessons of CLR provide a way to observe students' learning and evaluate the effectiveness of chosen curricula and materials. CLR is a way to address and examine all three aspects of curriculum as defined by Travers and Westbury (1989): "intended curriculum," "implemented curriculum," and "attained curriculum" (Figure 4.3.01). By meeting this criterion, CLR can be said to be a powerful way for a school to examine if the curriculum is being effectively implemented. In the same way that *Jyugyou Kenkyuu* has helped develop and refine TTP methods and materials in Japan over the years and continues to add to teaching and learning knowledge, CLR can help you adopt and expand TTP at your school. Japanese teachers use *Jyugyou Kenkyuu* to test the best way to implement new standards and curricula. You can use CLR to help you and your school meet demanding CCSS standards for mathematical practice which ask you to teach your students how to think mathematically.

We are working with numerous schools around the world to help them run CLR programs. For example, in 2015, we began piloting CLR at five elementary schools that teach kindergarten through eighth grade in an urban

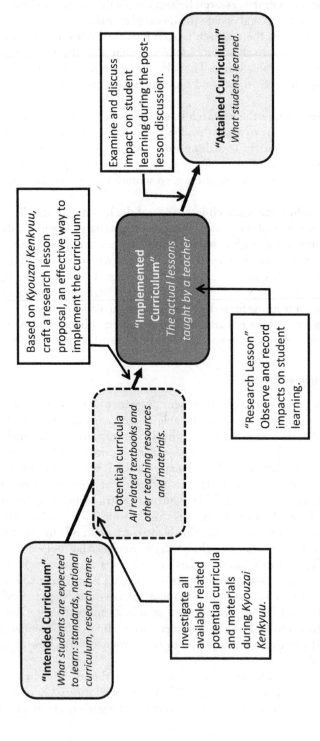

Figure 4.3.01 How CLR can address Travers and Westbury's (1989) three aspects of curriculum.

American school district (Takahashi & McDougal, 2018). We have already started to see positive changes. The following teacher statements are some examples:

> Lesson Study has enabled me to reflect upon my own teaching, not only individually, but within a supportive team. It has helped push me to be more introspective and ask myself the question "why" within my planning and instructional decisions.

> Lesson Study has completely changed my approach to mathematics instruction . . . My math pedagogical knowledge has increased tremendously. It is through Lesson Study that I've been able to truly reflect and gain insights into children's mathematical understandings/misunderstanding.

> We are loving Lesson Study. This could be transformative for our school. Analyzing research, creating lessons, and discussing student performance with other teachers is clearly the most productive professional development for a teacher. We clarified each other's misunderstandings as we read the material on fractions and discussed how ideas could be utilized in our classrooms. As teachers, we enriched our own understanding of fraction content and student perceptions . . . This Lesson Study has profoundly affected the activities I use.

> As I watched the lesson unfold I saw how, with good intentions, we teachers stop the thinking of our students by providing too much scaffolding . . . I saw students working themselves from an incorrect answer to recognizing the answer was wrong, puzzling over how to correct it, only to have a teacher ask "yes-no" questions that stopped their problem-solving and led [the students] to the correct answer. I recognize the trait in myself and have committed myself to allow the students time to struggle and . . . an opportunity to learn from mistakes. This will impact all of my instruction, not just fraction work.
>
> (Takahashi & McDougal, 2018)

CLR is helping these teachers improve their pedagogical skills for Teaching Through Problem-solving, thus helping their students meet CCSS for learning how to think mathematically.

The impact of CLR on students' improved capacity for learning mathematics and thinking mathematically is also clear. For example, at school A in this district, a pilot school which helped us develop CLR, growth in mathematics was measured at the 67th percentile (Takahashi & McDougal, 2016, p. 517). Also exciting was the mathematical conversations students were having in the classroom, "Even kindergarten students would present an idea, then turn to their classmates and ask if they agreed or disagreed" (Takahashi & McDougal, 2016, p. 517). At School C, CLR helped students, who are mostly second-language learners, continue to improve their scores on the state math test (Takahashi & McDougal, 2016). CLR also helped School E make dramatic changes at their school. In the beginning, only 50% of students met state standards for mathematics and reading; the entire staff was replaced (Takahashi & McDougal, 2016). We helped the new staff pick a research theme and initiate four teams to conduct CLR. End-of-year test scores put students in the 66th percentile, marking strong growth in mathematics (Takahashi & McDougal, 2016, p. 518). We continue to analyze the progress of school-wide CLR in these and other schools and will make the results available in the near future. Many of these schools are in urban, high-poverty areas. The promising results of CLR show that the program can help address issues of equity. Many teachers have been left alone in their classrooms and are expected to overcome teaching and learning challenges on their own. However, more and more schools around the world are recognizing the importance of ongoing professional development built into the regular school schedule. Research shows that teachers likely need to work together in order to effectively address teaching and learning issues unique to their students and schools (e.g., Stigler & Hiebert, 2009; Wei, Darling-Hammond, Andree, Richardson, & Orphanos, 2009). CLR provides the necessary framework for teachers to collaborate in this way. Teaching Through Problem-solving is built on the premise that students can make new discoveries and change the way they think and see the world by working together. In the same way, through Collaborative Lesson Research, you and your fellow teachers can work together to better understand how your students think and what they need. You can change your school.

References

Becker, J. P., & Miwa, T. (1987). *Proceedings of the U.S.–Japan Seminar on Mathematical Problem Solving (Honolulu, Hawaii, July 14–18, 1986)* (INT-8514988). Carbondale, IL: Southern Illinois University. Retrieved from www.academia.edu/21652649/Proceedings_of_the_U_S_Japan_Seminar_on_Mathematical_Problem_Solving_Honolulu_Hawaii_July_14_18_1986_

Becker, J. P., & Shimada, S. (1997). *The Open-ended Approach: A New Proposal for Teaching Mathematics.* Reston, VA: National Council of Teachers of Mathematics.

Becker, J. P., Silver, E. A., Kantowski, M. G., Travers, K. J., & Wilson, J. W. (1990). Some Observations of Mathematics Teaching in Japanese Elementary and Junior High Schools. *Arithmetic Teacher*, 38(2), 12–21.

Common Core State Standards Initiative. (2010). Common Core State Standards for Mathematics. Retrieved from www.corestandards.org/Math

Fujii, T. (2014). Implementing Japanese Lesson Study in Foreign Countries: Misconceptions Revealed. *Mathematics Teacher Education and Development*, 16(1), 65–83. Retrieved from www.merga.net.au/ojs/index.php/mted/article/view/206

Fujii, T. (2016). Designing and Adapting Tasks in Lesson Planning: A Critical Process of Lesson Study. ZDM, 1–13. doi:10.1007/s11858-016-0770-3

Lesson Study Alliance. (2020). Lesson Study Resources. Retrieved from www.lsalli
ance.org/resources/

Lesson Study Group at Mills College. (2018). Conduct a Cycle. Retrieved from https://
lessonresearch.net/conduct-a-cycle/overview/

Lewis, C. (2000). Lesson Study: The Core of Japanese Professional Development.
Paper presented at the AERA annual meeting, April.

Lewis, C., & Hurd, J. (2011). *Lesson Study Step by Step: How Teacher Learning Communities Improve Instruction.* Portsmouth, NH: Heinemann.

Lewis, C., Schaps, E., & Watson, M. (1995). Beyond the Pendulum: Creating Caring
and Challenging Schools. *Kappan*, 76, 547–554.

Lewis, C., & Tsuchida, I. (1997). Planned Educational Change in Japan: The Shift to
Student-centered Elementary Science. *Journal of Educational Policy*, 12, 313–331.

Lewis, C., & Tsuchida, I. (1998). A Lesson is Like a Swiftly Flowing River. *American
Educator* (Winter 1998), 12–51.

Makinae, N. (2019). The Origin and Development of Lesson Study in Japan. In R.
Huang, A. Takahashi, & J. da Ponte (Eds.), *Theory and Practice of Lesson Study in
Mathematics* (pp. 170–181). Berlin: Springer International Publishing.

Mullis, I. V. S., Martin, M. O., Beaton, A. E., Gonzalez, E. J., Kelly, D. L., & Smith, T.
A. (1997). *Mathematics Achievement in the Primary School Years: IEA's Third International Mathematics and Science Study (TIMSS).* Chestnut Hill, MA: IEA.

Murata, A., & Takahashi, A. (2002). *Vehicle To Connect Theory, Research, and Practice:
How Teacher Thinking Changes in District-level Lesson Study in Japan.* ERIC/CSMEE
Publications.

Project IMPULS International Math-teacher Professionalization Using Lesson Study.
(2011). Lesson Study Library. Retrieved from www.impuls-tgu.org/en/library/index.html

Seino, T., & Foster, C. (2020). Analysis of the final comments provided by a knowledgeable other in lesson study. *Journal of Mathematics Teacher Education.* doi:10.1007/
s10857-020-09468-y

Stevenson, H. (1980). The Polished Stones. Retrieved from www.youtube.com/
watch?v=Tpr6Q2FsJyE

Stevenson, H., & Stigler, J. (1992). *The Learning Gap.* New York: Summit.

Stigler, J., & Hiebert, J. (1999). *The Teaching Gap: Best Ideas from the World's Teachers
for Improving Education in the Classroom.* New York: Free Press.

Stigler, J., & Hiebert, J. (2009). Closing the Teaching Gap. *Phi Delta Kappan*, 91(3),
32–37.

Takahashi, A. (2014a). The Role of the Knowledgeable Other in Lesson Study: Examining the Final Comments of Experienced Lesson Study Practitioners. *Mathematics
Teacher Education and Development*, 16(1), 4–21. Retrieved from www.merga.net.au/
ojs/index.php/mted/article/view/204

Takahashi, A. (2014b). Supporting the Effective Implementation of a New Mathemat-
ics Curriculum: A Case Study of School-based Lesson Study at a Japanese Public
Elementary School. In I. Y. Li & G. Lappan (Eds.), *Mathematics Curriculum in School
Education* (pp. 417–441). New York: Springer.

Takahashi, A., & McDougal, T. (2016). Collaborative Lesson Research: Maximizing the Impact of Lesson Study. *ZDM Mathematics Education*, 48(4), 513–526.
doi:10.1007/s11858-015-0752-x

Takahashi, A., & McDougal, T. (2018). Collaborative Lesson Research (CLR).
In M. Quaresma, C. Winsløw, S. Clivaz, J. P. da Ponte, A. Ní Shúilleabháin, &

A. Takahashi (Eds.), *Mathematics Lesson Study Around the World: Theoretical and Methodological Issues* (pp. 143–152). Cham: Springer International Publishing.

Takahashi, A., & Yoshida, M. (2004). How Can We Start Lesson Study?: Ideas for Establishing Lesson Study Communities. *Teaching Children Mathematics*, 10(9), pp. 436–443.

Travers, K. J., & Westbury, I. (1989). The IEA Study of Mathematics I: Analysis of Mathematics Curricula. Supplement. Retrieved from https://eric.ed.gov/?id=ED306111

Watanabe, T., Takahashi, A., & Yoshida, M. (2008). Kyozaikenkyu: A Critical Step for Conducting Effective Lesson Study and Beyond. In F. Arbaugh & P. M. Taylor (Eds.), *Inquiry into Mathematics Teacher Education* (Vol. 5, pp. 131–142). Houghton, MI: Association of Mathematics Teacher Educators (AMTE).

Wei, R. C., Darling-Hammond, L., Andree, A., Richardson, N., & Orphanos, S. (2009). *Professional Learning in the Learning Profession: A Status Report on Teacher Development in the U.S. and Abroad*. Technical Report. National Staff Development Council.

Yoshida, M. (1999). Lesson Study: A Case Study of a Japanese Approach to Improving Instruction through School-based Teacher Development. Dissertation, University of Chicago, Chicago, IL.

Index